IT'S OKAY TO FAIL, MY SON

VASANT KALLOLA

IT'S OKAY TO FAIL, MY SON
Copyright ©Vasant Kallola, 2015

Printed in 2015

Published by
Bennett, Coleman & Co. Ltd.,
7, Bahadur Shah Zafar Marg,
New Delhi - 110002

Disclaimer
This book is a work of pure fiction, a figment of the author's imagination. TGB/BCCL will be free from any liability for damages and losses of any nature arising from or related to the content. All disputes are subject to the jurisdiction of competent courts in Delhi.

Published, Marketed & Distributed by

Times Group Books
(A division of Bennett, Coleman & Co. Ltd.)
Times Annexe, 9-10, Bahadur Shah Zafar Marg, New Delhi - 110002

Cover Illustration: Shiju George

Printed at: Gopsons Papers Ltd.

ISBN: 978-93-84038-75-5
Price: ₹299

Preface

IT WAS THE month of March. Year 2012, I suppose. Summer was setting in. On one such night, after one round of a good, short sleep, I woke up; I was thirsty. I looked at the wall clock.

It was 12.20am. I got up and walked towards the kitchen.

I walked down the corridor, and went past the study room in my house. I peeped in the room. Viraj, my son, was still awake, engrossed in his school textbook. 'Well, he must study hard,' I thought, 'this is his tenth standard, the foundation of his career.' Yet, I couldn't resist walking up to my son, to spend some time with him and cheer him up.

"Viraj, how is it going?" I asked.

He looked at me with sour red eyes; his tensed face and body language shook me from within! He did not say anything to me, simply smiled.

'This should not be the condition of my son,' I thought, 'whom I love the most in this world. This should not be the condition of a future leader – tensed, tired and fatigued – who has to win on many fronts in the future. This should not be the condition of future's all-powerful man, who has to carry forward my legacy and make me a proud father.'

3

"What's the matter? Are you enjoying your studies?"

To be honest, his answer was not very positive. Deep in thought, I walked out of his room, went to the kitchen and poured myself a glass of water. How many glasses of water had I drunk that night? I don't remember, frankly. I suppose I was deeply disturbed from within. I must have drunk more water than I needed to satiate my thirst! Whatever the case, one fact remains that I could not sleep properly that night (I am one of those lucky people who sleep well, and never lose sleep on any worldly matter; that night was an exception).

Seeing my son's condition that night, I was shaken to the core. I told myself that I must help him, give him courage. I must not burden him with my thoughts and expectations. On the contrary, I must create a situation which will make him enjoy his studies and not feel stressed out; help him develop skills that will enable him to excel in whatever he does or pursues in the future. I must free him from all inhibitions. I want to see him relaxed, confident and courageous – to take up every challenge he comes across in his life with joy, courage and happiness, with utmost liking and pleasure.

But if all this has to happen, some proactive steps have to be taken. First and foremost, Viraj will have to get rid of his fears: of failure, of not meeting the expectations of his parents and teachers, of his own doubts and insecurities. He must unlearn to learn. And for that unlearning to happen, as a father, guardian and guide to my growing son, I have to assure him that, "It's okay to fail, my son."

I have written this book not only for my son Viraj, but for children and people both in India and around the world who are leading stressful lives due to the excessive pressure thrust on them by all those around them: parents, teachers, friends, peers and all those known and unknown. This is equally applicable to people working in the corporate world, where people live under the constant stress of performance.

To make reading more interesting, I have presented it in the form of a story, of father and son, of teacher and students, weaving in the story the internationally acclaimed 'Mind Toughness Techniques'.

This is a novel that details how academically average students can turn out to be better than above-average students with the right inputs and support. It shows how learning capabilities of children can be dramatically improved with the right kind of environment, patience and motivation with slightly improvised methodologies. Finally, whatever one does, one must aim for excellence. And what is the point in excelling, if it is not exciting, enriching and joyful?

I am sure you will enjoy this novel. Please share your reviews, comments and suggestions with me. You can reach me through my email id – vkallola@gmail.com – and I will be glad to receive your suggestions and encouragement. That will be the next step of the strengthening of our relationship, my reader friend!

Warm regards,
Vasant Kallola

To my son, Viraj,
and millions of children
around the world, who are
in constant pursuit of excellence

The Rise of a Father

THUNDEROUS APPLAUSE ONCE again filled the hall. The Ball Room of the Taj Intercontinental Hotel, Mumbai, was full of people, attired in their best finery, in well-cut suits, gowns, and saris. The occasion was the Annual Business Awards Function of Mumbai's leading financial daily, *Global Economics & Analysis*. The who's who of Indian as well as internationally acclaimed business houses, in varied fields of businesses, be it real estate, manufacturing, power sector, software firms and whatnot, all rich and famous people had descended in the Taj's famous ballroom that day to participate in the event. The general talk in the corridor suggested that even to get an invitation to this event was a matter of privilege for business people.

The speaker on the dais, who had been making announcements related to the event, was the beautiful Priya Bhardwaj. Tall, extremely attractive and fair, she looked quite graceful in a dark red sari with a black sleeveless, backless blouse. Her stylish hairstyle too was drawing appreciative glances. After a few announcements, followed by a brief pause, she once again took the microphone in her hand and spoke into it.

"Welcome back, ladies and gentlemen, now let's move on to the most coveted award of the year. The award for this year's most innovative company goes to Gold Star Electronics for their development of the unique concept of Virtual Office, or V-Office. Although Gold Star is a US-based company, this concept has been conceived and developed by its Indian team headed by their outstanding CEO, Rahul Saxena. Ladies and gentlemen, please join me in welcoming Rahul Saxena on the stage."

Rahul Saxena, a smart, handsome young man in his early forties, got up from his seat, and slowly but confidently walked up to the stage. All eyes were fixed on Rahul, noting his gait, his attire and his confidence. Fair, well-built and of medium height, the main point of attraction in his personality was his eyes; playful and sparkling, they indicated a joyful nature and sharp mind. While walking to the stage, Rahul's straight posture hinted that he was a fitness freak. Needless to say, there were some in the room who became restless when they saw the young and suave CEO; others felt a sudden increase in their heartbeats after spotting the smart and gifted man.

Once he was up on the stage, Rahul shook hands with Priya and Shri Raj Shekhar Poddar, President of the jury, who was instrumental in selecting the awardee.

Raj Shekhar handed over the award, saying, "Congratulations, young man! You have not only made all of us proud but also given the world considerable hope of improving the quality of life of millions of citizens."

Taking the trophy, Rahul said, "Thank you, sir, for the honour."

As Rahul turned to go back to his seat, Priya quipped, "Congratulations, Rahul, for such a fantastic innovation, but we will not allow you to go back without hearing a few words from you," then she looked at the audience and said, "right?"

The audience responded enthusiastically, as if on cue. Rahul smiled and nodded his head in affirmation. She walked towards him and handed him the mic.

Holding the mic, Rahul looked at the trophy which he was holding in his right hand, smiled a bit and said, "Innovation is not new to Gold Star, because we love what we do," Rahul paused.

A round of applause greeted this statement.

He continued, "We always strive hard to give our customers and users a great experience, help them save on expenses and compete not only in India but across the world. Virtual Office – or V-Office – Concept, introduced for the first time by Gold Star, will redefine the way businesses are run. It is an application consisting of state-of-the-art hardware and software which are put together to facilitate all your business functions. V-Office will free people from the need to attend office every day; people will be able to operate from their homes and carry out business activities in a much more efficient way. This will free millions of people from the day-to-day routine of attending office in the conventional way, that is, travelling from home to the workplace and back, thereby helping companies, cities and countries save billions of dollars through better and smarter ways of conducting businesses.

"Let me tell you how we are going to transform your life and the budget of your companies, cities and countries and of the entire globe. At present, on every working day, all of us travel in the morning from our home to office, using either our own transport or the public transport. In office, we carry out our respective work and return home in the evening. According to the survey conducted by Gold Star, an average worker or executive spends two hours of travelling time to office, covering a distance of about 25km. He then works in office – which are generally air-conditioned spaces – and conducts his business. Do you realize the costs involved in making all of us work, out of our so-called, systematic office premises? Let me show you how much we spend."

He started explaining the details to the audience. The conclusions were that V-Office could save travelling costs of US$ 739 bn per annum; second, it could save office infrastructure investments to the tune of US$ 7,032 bn; and third, operational costs worth US$ 64.4 bn per annum could be saved as well.

Rahul continued, "Now going forward, if we assume 10 per cent more people are added to the global workforce, we will need an additional US$ 1,758 bn of investments in setting up new office premises, roads for travelling, fuel and several other essential resources. And we would need approx. US$ 263 bn per annum of operational costs to maintain the infrastructure. But, with our new solution, V-Office, you won't need all these – just a broadband connection and a computer at home. It's that simple! As a matter of fact, our new concept has the potential to alter the economies of several nations of the world."

As Rahul finished speaking, some people in the audience were so excited that they started clapping loudly. Before the applause could settle, the vice-president of the jury got up from his chair. His gesture inspired members of the audience to follow his lead: they too stood up, applauding, showing their admiration and appreciation. The standing ovation to Rahul's speech, the bright lights in the majestic hall, and the continuous flashlight from the cameras captured every moment with Rahul, which were some of the memories that every attendee of the function carried home with him that night.

The Troubled Son

SACHIN STOOD NERVOUSLY in the school principal's office. The principal was scolding Sachin, and the boy was listening, with his head down.

"What a shame, Sachin, month after month, your performance in school has been deteriorating. I have repeatedly told you to improve your grades but in vain. Look at your father; I can't believe you are the son of such a brilliant man. If this continues, I will have to talk to your parents," declared the principal.

Tensed and scared, Sachin slowly walked out of the principal's office. Out on the ground, Sachin's friends called out to him to play with them, but he hardly looked at them. He was confused, too, and hastily walked away, as if wanting to get away from school as quickly as possible. Soon, he reached home.

"So you've come!" quipped Aaya, as she threw open the entrance door for him.

He gave her a weak smile, and headed straight for his room. Aaya came in, behind him.

"Will you eat something now?"

"No, I'm not hungry," replied Sachin, and then, after a brief pause, "when will Dad come?"

"I don't know, but he will eat and come. He will be attending a function, so he will have his dinner there. He called up some time ago to ask about you."

Sachin looked disappointed. "I don't want to eat," he repeated angrily.

That night was really tough for Sachin. His father reached home quite late that night, and by that time, a tired and dispirited Sachin had fallen asleep.

Son of Rahul and Sheetal Saxena, Sachin is an innocent-looking boy with a slightly dark complexion and a lean body frame. Just last month, he had celebrated his thirteenth birthday. He was a student of Class IX, in Saraswati Vidhya Mandir School at Vile Parle, which is a suburb in Mumbai. Till some years back, when he lived with both his parents, Sachin was a very cheerful boy and a bright student; and a very happy family it was. But after his parents' divorce, it seemed as if his life had been divided in many parts...

Next morning, he woke up with a start, and almost ran to his father's room. He desperately wanted to talk to his father about his interaction with the principal. As he pulled open the door of the room, it opened with a big bang, but there was no one in the room. His father had already left for office!

Poor Sachin, he didn't know what to do!

★   ★   ★

Since the day he had been awarded by the industry, life had become even more hectic for Rahul Saxena, who had to leave home very early in the mornings. Even today, he wanted to meet his son. With that intention, he had peeped into Sachin's room before leaving for work, but Sachin was fast sleep. Reluctant to wake up his son, Rahul had kissed Sachin on his cheek and left.

At around 9am, Rahul got down from his chauffeur-driven car at the entrance of his office building. His office was in Worli, Mumbai. Located near the famous Television Tower, Gold Star's office consisted of three wings and 15 floors. As he entered the main lobby of the office, he saw the whole staff gathered there, to greet and welcome their favourite CEO. Smiling broadly, he stopped, pleased to see them in an upbeat mood.

Sunil Malhotra, HR Head, walked up to him with a bouquet of flowers and said, "Rahul, hearty congratulations for the award last night."

Middle-aged, medium height, fair and slightly heavy, Sunil reported to Rahul functionally, but on a personal level, they were very good friends.

Rahul took the bouquet and said, "Congratulations to you, Sunil, and all the staff of Gold Star Electronics. It is because of your hard work and contribution that we have achieved such an honour."

Staff members too looked quite excited to meet Rahul. He was surprised to see them forming a semicircle. Rahul walked up to each one of them and shook hands with them all.

After meeting his colleagues in the ground floor, Rahul took the lift that carried him to his office on the top floor of the building. As usual, copies of all leading newspapers had been neatly kept on his desk. He picked up one and started going through the pages. The news of Gold Star Electronics being awarded for V-Office was covered in detail with a photograph of Rahul receiving the award. The other newspapers too, had covered the event, in similar fashion. As Rahul was glancing through the papers, Nancy walked into his room.

"We all feel very proud today, sir," Nancy said.

Rahul smiled at her and said, "Yes. It is a matter of pride for all of us. Thank you for your support, Nancy."

'This gentleman keeps amazing me with his modesty,' Nancy thought, as she smiled in return.

"What's the schedule for today, Nancy?"

Nancy looked at her iPad and listed Rahul's agenda for the day. "First, at 11am, you have a meeting with the staff across India; I have been receiving many calls and messages from the staff about the recognition we got last night. At 3pm, there is a press conference and at 7pm there is an interview with News Broadcasting Company, which will be live telecast."

Though Rahul personally didn't approve of so much fanfare, but the board of Gold Star Electronics, the company he headed in India, wanted to make the most of the current situation. An interview had been scheduled that evening with the international business channel, NBC – News Broadcasting Company – of the UK. Tom Walter, an internationally acclaimed anchor, was supposed to conduct the interview.

At around 6pm, Rahul walked into the reception area of NBC's office, where he was warmly welcomed by Greta, Walter's secretary, who escorted him to Walter's cabin.

After exchanging pleasantries, Rahul and Tom went to the studio where the interview would be conducted, and sat down on the sofas meant for them. Rahul looked around; the programme director, Anupama Tyagi, was busy giving instructions to the cameramen. He also noticed an audience of around hundred people, in the studio. After finishing her work with the camera and light men, Anupama walked up to Rahul and greeted him. She checked if Rahul was comfortable and she could start the show. Rahul said he was ready to face the camera. She gave him a brief idea about how they would go about the interview, and told him that cameras would start rolling once she gives the signal.

As Anupama shouted, "Action!", cameras focused on Tom, who started talking to the viewers.

"Good evening, ladies and gentlemen. Today, I have the privilege of welcoming to our show, 'The Young Achievers Show', one of India's leading technocrats and business personalities, Rahul Saxena, the CEO of Gold Star Electronics. Recently, Rahul has introduced a new concept, V-Office or Virtual Office, which is likely to redefine the way businesses are conducted. According to Gold Star, it's going to make remarkable reductions in business expenditures, and will have an incredible impact on the quality of life of millions of office-goers who would benefit not only in saving their travelling costs and time, but will also be able to spend more time with their families and lead healthy, stress-free lives.

"So, ladies and gentlemen, please join me in welcoming Rahul Saxena to our today's business show."

Cameras changed angles to focus on Rahul and then zoomed back to cover the whole space where Rahul and Tom were sitting. Rahul waved at the audience with a smile on his face. He was wearing a steel grey jacket, a white shirt and black trousers.

Walter continued, "Rahul, welcome to the show. We would like you to tell us something about V-Office and how it will impact our lives."

"V-Office is based on broadband technology which uses the latest 4G network to connect people situated in different locations. Gold Star has developed an application, which will connect people, located thousands of miles away, with the same effectiveness as if they were all sitting in the same room. In technical terms, this is called Virtual Reality.

"This will eliminate the need to travel to office daily. Companies too will not feel the need to have multiple offices for their employees. With a small infrastructure at home or anywhere nearby, a person will be able to conduct his/her business operations, interact with one/many colleagues like they presently do in a meeting; give and take instructions/orders; share papers and drawings and carry out all other normal business transactions in a much more efficient way. In addition, the system can maintain all records of date, time of discussions, instructions given/taken, timelines agreed upon. And it will also give alarms, reminders to track the agreed plans/actions. Therefore, business transactions would be conducted seamlessly and in a well-organized way than the current form of office-based system.

"Now, think of the kind of savings it will bring about: to business entities, cities, countries and the entire globe! We can save millions of acres of land which we are currently using to house our office buildings and roads to carry people to and from the office. Besides the space, think of the billions of gallons of fuel which is consumed in transporting people to and from office. Apart from better utilization of existing infrastructure, we can free society from creating new infrastructure of office buildings, roads, bridges and public transport systems. Just imagine how changed the world would be if these saved resources can be used in building gardens, parks, lakes, and in the natural world."

Walter's eyes were widening with every sentence that Rahul uttered, as if he wanted to catch every word, every movement of

Rahul's, like a small child who was experiencing the wonder of some technological marvel for the first time. Walter was absolutely excited.

"This sounds amazing, Rahul... if I talk about my own life, I can save at least 2-2.5 hours of my travelling time every day. In other words, I can sleep for an hour more, use 30 minutes to do my exercise which I generally miss because I have to rush to office. And wow, in the remaining one hour I can drop my son to his school and even do my work more efficiently because I'm not tired as I'll be free from the regular struggles of running, jostling in train/traffic before I reach office."

At the back of his mind, Walter's thoughts flitted to his increased flirtations with his son's beautiful teacher! But reminding himself that he was in the midst of an interview, he brought his mind back to the studio.

Rahul smiled, "Exactly, Tom! This is not only true for you but for almost a billion people living on this planet. All the monies that we could be spending in building office space, building new roads, bridges and public transport systems, can be used in building and maintaining parks and orchards for our children. Lakes which can not only beautify our cities, but also help us solve our water problem. Billions of dollars saved in fuel can change our entire economy from trade deficit to surplus. In short, we can gift our children a far more livable planet."

At this statement, there was thunderous applause from the live audience in the studio. It lasted for almost 2-3 minutes, as if those present did not want to stop clapping, despite several requests from Walter.

"Rahul, I'm really impressed with your highly promising and inspiring vision. I sincerely wish your vision turns into reality and we all live a very healthy and peaceful life."

Rahul nodded confidently, "It will – why doubt it?"

One member of the audience raised his hand. A camera immediately focused on him. It was a young man.

Walter looked at him and asked, "Is there something you'd like to say?"

When he nodded, Walter said, "Go ahead."

"Sir, the picture you have drawn is too good to believe, and I sincerely wish we can achieve it. But I have a question…?"

"Please go ahead," Rahul nodded encouragingly.

"If we stop building new roads, bridges, cars, won't our progress get impacted?"

Rahul looked at him and asked, "May I know your name?"

"Srinivas."

Rahul explained, "I agree that roads, bridges and other essential infrastructure play a supporting role in the development of a country, and we could continue to build infrastructure that can support our growth. But, Srinivas, roads and bridges are not the only things we need; we also need to focus on telecom, ports, manufacturing and irrigation capabilities to support our growth requirements. While not discounting the need to build infrastructure, what I am saying is that we must use technology to its full potential and avoid unproductive activities such as commuting to office every day.

"Now, looking at your question on progress from another angle, what do you mean by progress of a society?"

Srinivas looked a bit uncertain, tried to find an answer but didn't say anything. So Rahul spoke, perhaps to help Srinivas find an answer.

"In my opinion, the true reflection of the progress of any society is the happiness, health and well-being of its people.

Happiness means that people live a stress-free and relaxed life. Every human being should get proper food, shelter and medicines. Right?"

Srinivas nodded in affirmation.

Rahul continued, "But do you know that today, 16 per cent of the world's population is going to bed without a proper meal twice a day, that millions of people are not getting the opportunity to study, and a large number of children are victims of malnutrition? This is not the world we would like to see. In our so-called modern society today, people are hassled. You add roads but faster than that you add traffic; you build houses, but today in a city like Mumbai, a decent 2-BHK house is out of reach of almost 70 per cent of the population. There can be an argument that you get easy finances from banks and institutions, but houses have become extremely costly. Once you take a loan, you have invited tension for the next 15–20 years – in other words, you have mortgaged your youth to financial institutions!

"Let's talk about health. It is due to the stress caused by the present lifestyle that people are becoming victims of life-threatening diseases. Almost 16 per cent of the world's population is victim to hypertension and diabetes. In the last three decades, the cost of building a house has increased by 1000 per cent but sperm count among men has reduced to 20 million per ml, one-third of what it was thirty years ago. So, the rotation of money has increased dramatically in the system, which has resulted in an increase in salaries and wages, but your houses have become smaller, you have become weaker and vulnerable to diseases. Leave aside physical diseases, even mental diseases have dramatically increased in our society. In short, in my opinion, so-called progress has made us less happy, fragile and more dependent on outside systems for our own survival. I feel there is an urgent need to change that."

As soon as Rahul finished talking, there was a big round of applause which continued for some time.

*   *   *

Sachin was watching his father on the TV. But there was no expression on his face.

In another part of the city, someone else was also watching Rahul's interview on the TV, but switched it off, muttering to herself, "Bullshit! Why is it that your talks are always beyond my understanding?! I hope someday you will talk sense, Rahul."

Mrs Rahul Saxena, or Sheetal Mehra Saxena – Rahul's ex-wife and Sachin's mother – was a modern, beautiful lady, and a lawyer by profession; perhaps her argumentative nature had contributed in some measure to her success in her chosen career. Rahul and Sheetal had divorced two years back (after 15 years of married life) and she had since then shifted to her own apartment in Bandra. The daughter of a very successful lawyer in Mumbai, Sheetal managed her own legal practice in her Lower Parel office.

"Forget it, I have a very important case in court tomorrow. I have to get up early," murmuring to herself she left the drawing room and went to her bedroom.

The next day in a corridor of the family court, Sheetal walked alongside her client, assuring her.

"Look, Shilpa, your case is very strong. You have all the reasons to leave Sudhir and seek divorce. He has to consider your requirements and keep your interests in mind; after all he has married you. His argument that he can't leave his family is a lame excuse. Why can't he leave his mother and brother, and live

20

separately with you? We have a very strong case in our favour, Shilpa, and I'm sure you will be able to get justice in court."

After some time, they stood near the courtroom where their case would be heard, waiting for their turn. After about 15 minutes, the name of Shilpa Phadake was announced. Sheetal and Shilpa entered the courtroom, and took their respective seats. Shilpa's husband Sudhir, and his lawyer, Bankim, also entered the courtroom, and sat down. The judge was busy reading some papers. Sheetal waited for him to get free. After a while, he looked up at Sheetal and nodded, giving permission to start her argument.

Sheetal presented her case confidently, "Your Honour, my client Mrs Shilpa Sudhir Phadake has filed a case against her husband Sudhir and his mother Mrs Sulakshnadevi Phadake for physical labour, mental torture and harassment. Under the Indian Penal Code, she wants to divorce Sudhir, so that she can lead an independent, trouble-free life."

The judge announced solemnly, "You may proceed with your case."

"Your Honour, my client Shilpa is married to Sudhir for the past four years. They stay in a joint family, along with Sudhir's mother, his elder brother and his elder brother's wife. The elder brother has retired and, therefore, does not have an income of his own. In a way, he and his family are a liability on Sudhir; my client has repeatedly told her husband that they should live separately from them, in another house, which Sudhir has refused to do. My client has waited for many years but now she is not able to live under the same conditions, and is seeking divorce from Sudhir. You are requested to grant them divorce so that she can lead an independent and dignified life."

Sudhir's lawyer, Bankim, stood up and said, "Your Honour, I would like to question Shilpa."

"You may proceed."

Shilpa got up from where she was sitting in the courtroom, and walked towards the witness box. Once in the witness box, she faced Bankim. Adjusting his gown, Bankim walked towards Shilpa, looked at her in the eyes for a few seconds, and then proceeded with his questions.

"Ma'am, do you have parents?" and then quickly added, "what a silly question, you can't be born without parents. I mean, are your parents alive?"

"My dad passed away three years back, Mum stays in Kolkata."

"How old is she?"

"Seventy-five," Shilpa replied.

"Does she stay alone? Or is there a caretaker? I mean, is there some young person in the house who takes care of her needs, safety, etc."

"No, she stays in my father's flat, all alone. I have a brother but he lives separately, with his family. You see, we are a modern family, everyone is independent and leads his or her own life the way they wish to. We neither interfere in other's lives, nor do we like interference in our lives," Shilpa said emphatically.

"Last year, your mother suffered a cardiac arrest and she was unconscious in her house. Luckily, she has a good and caring young couple as her neighbour, who reached your mother's flat on time and took her to the hospital. Don't you think she would be better off by not being left alone? Would you not like your own brother to take care of your mother in her hour of need? After all, she gave birth to him, brought him up, and made him capable of looking after himself, his family and leading the life he is leading at present?"

Shilpa looked down and said quietly, "Yes."

Turning to look at the judge, Bankim said, "Point to be noted, Your Honour."

Bankim continued, "Do you have any children?"

"No."

"I understand you had two miscarriages in the last three years. Is it true?"

Sheetal immediately stood up and protested, "I object, Your Honour. This question has no relevance to the case; Mr Bankim is misguiding my client."

"No, Your Honour, I am driving home a point which is relevant to the case."

The judge looked at Sheetal, and said, "Objection overruled," and then said to Bankim, "you may continue."

"Thank you, Your Honour."

Moving towards Shilpa, Bankim asked, "Please answer my question, you had two miscarriages in the last three years, yes or no?"

"Yes."

"You recovered quickly only because of the extra care and home-remedy medicines given by your mother-in-law and Bhabhi. Yes?"

Shilpa was silent, and when Bankim insisted that she respond, she replied, "I appreciate it but that could have been done even by my maidservant."

Everyone in the court was shocked, including the judge, but before Bankim or anyone could react, the judge announced that time was up and he adjourned the court, till the next hearing.

Coming out of the court, Sheetal had a big smile on her face, as if she had achieved something great, while Shilpa seemed preoccupied; maybe she was confused. On the other hand, Sudhir looked miserable, his eyes expressing his pain and haplessness. He looked at Bankim, who did not know what to say.

*   *   *

Sachin's steadily deteriorating academic performance, eventually prompted Principal Roshan Daruwala to summon him to his office, again.

Looking annoyed, the principal spoke sternly, "Sachin, your academic performance is becoming worse every month. You were once a brilliant child but I can't understand why you are scoring so poorly in your studies nowadays. You must bring your parents to school tomorrow, I want to meet them immediately."

"But, sir…"

"No, I don't want to listen to any excuses this time."

"Okay, sir," said Sachin and left the principal's office.

He didn't know what to do, and felt helpless and lonely. As he was walking past the school ground, he heard someone calling out to him.

"Hey, Sachin!"

He looked around to see Samir, his best friend in school, but today even Samir could not cheer him up.

Samir walked up to him, looking concerned, and asked, "Why are you looking so scared and miserable, what's happened?"

"Principal Sir has asked me to get my parents tomorrow to school, but my dad is in the US."

"Then you should have told him so."

"He isn't ready to listen. I don't know what to do!"

24

"Get your mother instead," advised Samir.

Sachin shook his head in disagreement as if he knew it wouldn't work out either.

"You don't know my mother, Samir. If she comes here, the situation will become more difficult for me."

"Then what are you going to do?"

"Don't know. Let's see," answered Sachin, taking a deep breath.

Later in the day, and after thinking a lot and not finding any alternative, Sachin finally called up his mother.

"Hello?" Sheetal answered her phone.

"Hello, Mum," responded Sachin.

"Yes, Sachin, how are you? How are your studies going? How did you do in the last exam? What marks did you get in mathematics? You did well in science, I hope?" she started throwing question after question at Sachin, who didn't know what to do, what to say.

The questions made Sachin even more anxious, and his hands as well as voice started trembling.

"Mum, you have to come to school tomorrow. Principal Sir has asked me to bring my parents to meet him."

Abruptly, the tone of her voice became harsh and loud.

"Why has he called me? What have you done? Despite all my suggestions and advise, you're not improving at all. Every second day, I keep hearing complaints about you. I am fed up of all this! You have no shame at all."

Her attack was so powerful that it was enough to fill tears in Sachin's eyes. He listened for some time without responding.

Suddenly she demanded, "Well, why don't you tell me why he has called? I know, you are not so clever that he would have called me to his office to give me an award. He'll be again complaining about you, am I right, Sachin? Why aren't you speaking up?"

"Mum, I haven't got good marks in the exams, that's why," Sachin said, sounding low. "I don't know why I got such poor marks, I had put in a lot of effort, Mum," Sachin replied helplessly.

His mother shouted over the phone, "I don't know anything! Why did you get less marks? Look at the other students. Look at your cousins... they are all doing well in their studies, aren't they?"

With the passing of every minute, Sheetal was becoming more and more restless, passing her anxiety on to Sachin through taunts, without realizing what impact it could have on her son's tender mind. Sachin, of course, had no option but to listen to this endless bombarding!

"Now tell me," Sheetal commanded, "when do we have to go? By the way, where is your dad? Why don't you take him along, he has only spoiled you."

"Mum, Dad is in the US. He had to attend some conference. Mum, I'm sorry, but will you come, please?"

"Do I have any option?" she replied derisively.

The moment the conversation was over, Sachin could not ascertain if his Mum would accompany him to school or not. This uncertainty, combined with nervousness, brought tears to his eyes. 'There is no one to support me,' he thought. Sachin looked at a photograph of a smiling Rahul, who wasn't around....

★　★　★

Meanwhile, in the US, Rahul's contributions to business and the stock market performance of the company were well appreciated by the board members of Gold Star Electronics. The company had called a board meeting and he was a special invitee. In the board meeting, Chairman David Brown took his seat; all board members were also seated. Rahul was one of them.

"Good morning, gentlemen, welcome to our board meeting," David Brown greeted all members.

Looking around at the members, Brown said, "Today is a special day in the history of Gold Star Electronics – we have Rahul Saxena with us. Rahul is one of our brightest employees and he heads Indian operations. I am pleased to share with you that we have got an overwhelming response from the market for our innovative solution V-Office, conceived, designed, developed and introduced by Rahul's team in India. I am sure all of you are aware of V-Office and what benefits it can offer to user organizations."

With a broad smile on his face, he looked at all the board members, who were also in smiles.

He concluded his address by adding, "Needless to say, with this solution, Gold Star will become industry leader in revenue and profitability.

"I request you to join me in welcoming Rahul to our global board as a distinguished member. I am sure his experience, innovative mindset and researches will bring greater success and glory to our group."

The board members applauded, signifying their approval of Rahul's inclusion in the global board.

Acknowledging the recognition given to him, Rahul said, "David, board members, it is an honour to be a part of this unique group, which is well known the world over for its competency, business acumen and strategies. Today, the world is facing a unique challenge of deteriorating environment. We believe we have made a lot of progress since the age of industrialization, but the fact is that our lives have become more confined within boundaries of the progress we have achieved. We have lost our childhood, houses have become smaller, play grounds have almost vanished, rivers have been replaced with gutters, and forests have been replaced by concrete jungles.

"We are increasingly getting entrapped in diseases like hypertension, cancer and HIV/AIDS. While we are finding cures for some diseases, new ones keep appearing as if there is a constant chase. Indeed, life itself has become a chase, resulting in a significant loss of pleasures associated with life. V-Office is an attempt to find a solution. I'm sure it will prove to be the first significant step in the direction of solving problems faced by mankind."

He sipped some water and continued, "Being given this opportunity to work with you gentlemen, I can assure you that I will constantly strive to achieve greater success and glory for Gold Star."

David got up from his seat and shook hands with Rahul; this was followed by other board members, and everyone congratulated Rahul on his achievement and for the promise he brought with him.

The company had arranged a press conference for Rahul the next day. As he was getting ready for the press meet, his mobile rang.

"Oh, it's Sachin," he murmured, recognizing the number.

He answered the call, "Hello, my son, how are you?"

"Hello Dad, it's me," said Sachin nervously.

Rahul could sense Sachin's nervousness on phone and got concerned. "Son, what's the matter? Are you alright? Why are you upset? Is there anything you want from the US? I will bring back some interesting gifts for you."

"Dad, please come back now. I need you here!" pleaded Sachin.

"I understand, son, but you have to realize that it's just not possible for me to leave everything here just now and come to India. I have to finish some work and then I will certainly go back, we will have a great time together, Sachin," Rahul tried to cheer him up.

On the other side, Sachin could not control his emotions and started to sob. The initial small sobs and gulps grew louder and uncontrollable, which really worried Rahul.

"Sachin, my son, how come such a brave boy is crying! What's the matter?"

Sachin told him about his deteriorating performance in school, the principal getting upset with him and asking his parents to meet him. Sachin also briefed him about his interaction with Sheetal, his mother. Rahul asked him to relax, promising that he would talk to Sheetal and ask her to accompany him to meet the principal.

*   *   *

Sheetal was in her office when her mobile phone rang. She looked at the mobile's screen, and her eyebrows rose. It was Rahul.

"Hello, Mr Rahul Saxena! How is it that you are thinking of me today?" she greeted him sarcastically.

Rahul ignored the sarcasm and replied, "I think of you every day, you are the one who has closed the doors of communication, and that's not allowing my voice and emotions to reach you."

"Oh, I see. Are you sure?" she continued with her sarcasm. "You have never telephoned me unless there is some work. I'm sure that even today you are calling me up for some work...?"

"Look, Sheetal, I wanted to talk to you about Sachin. He spoke to me some time back and I think he needs us. I'm in the US and can't come back to India right now. Can you please accompany him to meet his school principal?"

"Why does it have to be me, every time? If you are busy, then so am I. He is not only my son, he is yours too!" Sheetal snapped.

"Yes, of course, he is our son and hence I am equally responsible for his well-being as you are, but currently I'm in the US for some urgent work and I can't leave midway. You are in Mumbai, and can therefore make it to the meeting. Could you please attend the meeting with the principal?" requested Rahul politely.

Sheetal seemed to be in a mood to fight, but Rahul's soft approach forced her to change her mind and she replied, "Okay, sir, but don't make it a habit to throw all your responsibilities at me."

After disconnecting her phone, she called up Sachin and fixed a time for meeting the principal.

Next day, when she went to pick up Sachin from his home, she was frowning. Sachin was ready when she reached his place. He got into the car and greeted her warmly.

"Good morning, Mum."

"What is good this morning?" she asked him sharply.

Such a rough reaction was enough to make Sachin nervous, which was visible on his face and in his body language.

"Yes tell me, what's the matter?"

"Mum, Principal Sir called me to his room because of my low marks in maths, and that's why he wants to talk to you."

"Why is it that month after month, your marks are dropping?"

Sachin opened his mouth to explain, but her scolding stopped him halfway.

"What do you do in school the whole day? Play games, right?"

"No, Mum," Sachin replied timidly.

"I have warned you several times that I will not tolerate poor performance in academics, but you just don't listen! You're wasting time in useless activities."

"No, Mum, I got poor marks in maths because I don't understand it. Geometry is very difficult and despite my very best, I just can't grasp it," pleaded Sachin with teary eyes.

"Okay, okay, no drama please," Sheetal stopped him, annoyed. "I have no interest in such drama. You must demonstrate success and intelligence in your performance. Dumb people have no place in today's world."

'Mum is very hard, she never tries to understand my difficulties and just pushes me to do better without really bothering to find out my problems,' Sachin thought unhappily.

Four people were present in the principal's office: Principal Roshan Daruwala himself, Sachin's class teacher Ms Madhuri, Sheetal and Sachin.

The principal began, "Madam, I'm sorry to trouble you, but it was essential to meet you, to talk to you about Sachin's future. What I'm surprised about is that he used to be a very bright student till he was in Class VII, but in the last two years his academic performance has been deteriorating and all our efforts and counselling have not made any difference. I'm really worried, and so I called this meeting to apprise you about his performance and understand if there are any issues on the family front that are bothering him."

Sheetal listened to him silently.

Then Ms Madhuri added, "Even in class he is withdrawn. He remains aloof; earlier he used to play, participate in class activities and would also be mischievous sometimes, but not anymore. He keeps to himself, speaks only if spoken to, does not smile much. Yet, at times, he is extraordinarily bright. Just last week I had asked all the students to write an essay on their hero and Sachin wrote a superb essay on his father."

"Thank you very much for your inputs, I'm worried about Sachin, too. I did notice his poor grades in class, but I thought it to be a temporary affair and advised him. I will give him more time and help him do better in his studies," Sheetal said.

Madhuri asked curiously, "Sachin is very fond of his dad, how is he? Why didn't he come along with you?"

On hearing this, Sheetal grew angry and said, raising her voice, "He is not in India, that's the reason why I had to come here today. Anyway, I will talk to him and we will do our best to improve Sachin's grades!"

"Oh, okay but it will be a pleasure to meet him, if there's a next time," Madhuri smiled a little as she said this, "please do bring him along. He seems to be very intelligent. Recently I saw his interview on NBC, where he spoke about his invention of V-Office and how it can transform our planet and improve the quality of life we lead."

All this while, Sheetal had been trying to control her temper, but hearing Rahul being praised so much, she blurted out rudely, "We don't stay together and, by the way, I'm not his secretary, so I don't have to agree with him on whatever he talks or does. He has a habit of talking big. Let's see."

Both Madhuri and the principal were taken aback, while Sachin squirmed in his seat, uneasily.

Sheetal carried on, furious, "It is because of the extra-busy, intelligent and smart Mr Saxena that Sachin is in the condition that you see him today. Even my condition is not good. He has all the time for the world, but not for his family!"

As she continued criticizing Rahul, Sachin who had been silent so far, mildly protested, "Mama, please don't say anything about Dad. I love him."

"See, look at this... even our son is on his side. I take all the trouble to come and meet you. There is no appreciation for it, but the moment I speak against his dad, Sachin has to object!" Sheetal ranted on.

Thanks to Sheetal's bitter words, Principal Roshan Daruwala realized the tension between Sheetal and Rahul.

He politely but firmly told her, "Well, er, Mrs Saxena, we have conveyed the facts which I feel you should know about your son. Try and support him, he does not seem to be in the right frame of mind. I don't know the reasons behind it. What I can definitely see is that he needs counselling, comfort and love. Children are like tender plants, with care and proper environment you can make them blossom, but under harsh conditions they can create some situations which we can only regret, if ignored. Okay then, I have to go for my class. Thanks for coming, it was nice meeting you," he stood up, signalling the end of the meeting.

On the way back from school, Sheetal was still seething – her ego was hurt. She couldn't accept the few firm words that the principal had said towards the end of the meeting. She obviously had not taken the message and concerns expressed by the principal and Madhuri in the right spirit. Her mind was wandering around Rahul's popularity, the appreciation he was getting for his innovation and the manner in which the principal had wrapped up the meeting. She took it as an insult! And her fault-finding mindset had interpreted things in a totally different way, leaving no space or even thought for supporting or counselling Sachin. Poor Sachin!

As the car headed towards Sachin's home, Sachin became a victim to Sheetal's annoyance.

"It is all because of you that I have to listen to all this crap. Had you been responsible unlike your father, I would have been a proud mother today. They would not have treated me the way they did!"

Sachin's tender mind was not able to comprehend the developments around him. He just looked more confused.

He just sighed, "Come back soon, Dad."

⋆　⋆　⋆

The maths class was in progress. Bhattacharya Sir was teaching geometry to the class.

Suddenly he stopped to ask a question to the class, and his eyes fell on Sachin.

"What is the equation of the area of a circle?"

Sachin stood up, a blank look on his face; he couldn't answer the question.

Annoyed, Bhattacharya Sir started yelling at Sachin, "You don't know such a simple answer? What do you do in class? Where is your attention?"

Then, he looked at another student and asked, "Shivani, you tell me, what is the equation of the area of a circle?"

Shivani promptly replied, "Pi r square, sir."

Nodding, the teacher looked at Sachin again, "See, how simple it is? You don't know the answer to even such a simple question?"

Sachin started fidgeting. He stuttered, "Sa-sa-ra actually…"

"What actually?" Bhattacharya Sir thundered. "Show me your note book. Have you written the notes I had given in class?" and he strode towards Sachin's desk.

He picked up Sachin's note book and found it blank. This was enough for all hell to break loose upon the boy.

"Get up, get up from your chair. Get out of my class!"

Slowly Sachin got up from his seat and walked out of the classroom.

He murmured, "Come back soon, Dad."

The Ultimate Step

AN AMBULANCE RUSHED through the busy streets of Mumbai, its wailing siren forcing the other vehicles on the road to move aside, giving way to it. It stopped outside Mahajan Hospital, and an attendant hurriedly got down from the ambulance and pulled the rear door, which the paramedic team, seated inside, had partially pushed open. Assisted by other hospital staff, they quickly but carefully removed a stretcher, on which lay a young boy, unconscious. It was Sachin Saxena!

The Emergency staff of the hospital swung into action and rushed him to the Emergency Ward. By the time the doctors present conducted a preliminary examination, and put Sachin on initial treatment, Dr Amit Mahajan came running to the ward. He too examined Sachin and gave some instructions to the nurse on duty. In the next few moments, Sachin was taken to the operation theatre.

Sheetal, who had left for the hospital the moment she got the news, rushed into the Emergency Ward, but was told that Dr Mahajan was treating Sachin at that very moment, and she was asked to wait outside, at the waiting area. When Dr Mahajan walked out of the OT after around two hours, the hospital staff called out to Sheetal.

Tensed and scared, she virtually ran to him, and asked, "How is Sachin, Dr Mahajan?"

"Can't say right now, Ma'am, we are doing our best. We are keeping him under observation now," the doctor said, and turned to speak to one of the nurses.

Sheetal was in tears and started crying inconsolably. Suddenly, she remembered something. She wiped her tears, took out her mobile phone, and dialled a number.

After some time, a voice at the other end of the line, responded, "Hello!"

"Rahul? Sheetal this side. I have some very bad news."

Rahul was immediately on alert, "What happened?"

Sheetal's voice broke as she spoke, "Sachin has committed suicide," and then with another burst of tears, she added, "he consumed poison. Right now he is under observation, he has just been operated upon. Please come back immediately!"

Rahul was in a meeting with David when Sheetal broke the news to him. The mobile phone slipped out of Rahul's hand, and darkness enveloped him. Rahul felt as if the ground beneath his feet was shaking. He wanted to speak but no words came out of his mouth, just some unclear sound.

David noticed the sudden change in Rahul's face, and realized that he had received some horrifying news. He quickly filled a glass of water from the bottle kept on his desk, and offered it to Rahul. David noticed Rahul was not in a position to hold the glass, so he held Rahul's head in his left hand and took the glass, filled with water, in his right hand near Rahul's mouth. After some time, Rahul seemed to be recovering; he sipped some water and closed his eyes. Rahul rested his head on the back of the chair. Tears trickled down Rahul's cheeks.

David sat quietly, wondering what had happened, and waited for Rahul to gain composure. When he had calmed down somewhat, David asked him what had happened. With moist eyes and in a trembling voice, Rahul apprised him of the situation.

David said, "I'm very sorry for you, Rahul, but everything will be alright, don't lose hope."

Then he looked at his watch and, thinking fast, continued, "At this time, there's no flight to India. Do one thing. You take my plane and leave, right away. I'll just call the aviation ministry and arrange your travel to India."

He got up from his chair, came closer to Rahul, put his hand on Rahul's shoulder and said, "I want you to stop doubting, and believe that your son will be alright."

Moved, Rahul looked at him and said, "Thanks, David. I hope your words turn out to be true."

After around 30 hours, Rahul landed at Chhatrapati Shivaji International Terminus in Mumbai. After completing landing formalities, he sat in a car which drove him to Mahajan Hospital.

When he arrived at the hospital, there was a long queue at the lift. Sheetal had informed him that Sachin had been allotted a special room on the seventh floor of the hospital. Rahul could not wait for the lift to arrive and virtually ran up the stairs. By the time he reached the seventh floor, he was exhausted, and in spite of being a fitness freak, such was his state that he was breathing heavily and perspiring. But he didn't care!

With his throat dry, perspiring, and heavy breathing, Rahul paced the corridor, his eyes searching for Sheetal. Then he saw her, standing at a corner, looking out of the window, perhaps in deep thought. Rahul moved closer to her and put his hand on her back. She turned, looked up. Her eyes had swollen due to excessive crying, her face was pale; perhaps she hadn't slept well the previous night.

She put her head on Rahul's chest and started crying loudly. After a while, she took hold of herself. In a choked voice, she told Rahul, "Sachin consumed poison to commit suicide."

Tears welled up in Rahul's eyes. It was with tremendous effort that he controlled his emotions, but deep sadness and worry were visible on his face. Sheetal took Rahul to Sachin's room.

"How is he?" without moving his gaze from Sachin, Rahul asked her.

"He is out of danger now, but may take a few days to recover."

In a choked, trembling voice, Rahul asked, "Why did Sachin take such a step?"

Sheetal remained silent.

After an hour, the doctor came on the floor again, on his rounds. At that time, Rahul was outside Sachin's room, his mind blank. Seeing the doctor, Rahul recognized him; he had met Dr Mahajan in one of the functions where he had been invited as guest.

As the doctor came near Sachin's room, Rahul asked him, "Hello, Amit, how is Sachin?"

"Oh, Rahul, is he your son?"

"Yes, Amit, can you please tell me about his condition now?"

"Well, Rahul, he has consumed poison," Dr Mahajan began gravely. "And he arrived in hospital quite late. We have given him the required medications and treatment, and are waiting for him to respond to it. So far, there has been very little improvement in his condition since the time he was brought in. I think it could have been better, so we are observing him. Let's hope for the best, Rahul."

"Amit, it's a little odd to ask, but do you think Sachin is safe here? I mean, do you need any support from doctors in the US, or any other place in the world?"

"No, Rahul. I don't think there's any need for that. He is in the best hands. Don't worry, Rahul. Just pray that we are successful in our efforts and may God bless Sachin with fast recovery."

Then, after thinking for some time, Dr Mahajan asked, "What happened? Why did your son take such a step?"

"I really don't know. I was in the US when my wife telephoned me. I've come here straight from the airport. I really don't know why Sachin would think of killing himself," Rahul replied, looking weary and haggard, gazing at the distance.

Then, exhaling slowly, he added, "God, please be kind to me. Give long life to my son, take mine in exchange, if you so desire."

Dr Amit Mahajan, who as a doctor was used to such kind of cases happening daily in the hospital, was moved by Rahul's grief and pain.

Trying to console him, Dr Mahajan patted Rahul's shoulder, and said, "Don't worry, God will surely be kind to a gentleman like you," and moving forward, entered Sachin's room.

Unable to do anything, Rahul stayed out on the corridor, and stared blankly at the door, which had closed some time back.

★ ★ ★

A police inspector walked up to where Rahul was sitting with Sheetal.

"Are you Sachin Saxena's father?"

"Yes," replied Rahul.

"I am Inspector Javed Khan," the inspector introduced himself, "I'm in charge of the Vile Parle Police Station. I need to know what exactly had happened. Why did the boy take such a step?"

"Inspector, I really don't know. I was in the US, when my wife, Sheetal," gesturing at Sheetal, Rahul added, "called me and broke the news. I reached Mumbai this morning and came here straight from the airport."

Inspector Khan turned towards Sheetal, "Then you must know, ma'am. Can you please tell me why has he taken such a step? What happened that pushed him into taking his life?"

"I'm sorry, I too don't know how exactly it happened. I was sleeping when I received a call from the servant at home that Sachin was lying on the bed, unconscious, foaming at the mouth. I telephoned the hospital and asked them to rush an ambulance. Just as the ambulance reached the house, I also reached the house where Sachin lives."

"Do you mean to say Sachin had gone to stay with someone?" the inspector asked, looking puzzled, and stopped writing on his note book, where he had been jotting down Sheetal's statement.

"No, Sachin was at home only."

"Oh, you must have gone to stay with someone... who... your mother or...?" he left the sentence incomplete.

"No, I was at my house."

Now the inspector really looked confused.

"Wait a minute. You said you were at your house, Sachin was also at his house, but then how come you are saying you don't know what happened to him? Are you joking with me in such a situation?" he was on the verge of losing his cool.

Rahul intervened, "Sorry, inspector, she doesn't stay with me. We are separated, and Sachin, out of his choice, stays with me. I was in the US, so neither of us really know what happened."

In the meantime, news of Sachin's attempted suicide had spread in the city, and in Sachin's school. Hearing the news, the school principal and Sachin's class teacher Ms Madhuri, too, had come running to the hospital.

As the inspector was talking to Rahul and Sheetal, the principal and Madhuri walked up to Rahul, asking about Sachin's condition.

"*Ticha Maila! Aata samjhlo. Aapan* modern *maa baap hai. Padhe-likhe*, intelligent but *ahamkari. Aap logon ka* emotion *se zyada bada* ego *hota hai tabhi toh bachche ke paas koi nahin tha. Bachcha bechara kya karega*? (Oh Mother Beater! Now I understand. You are well-educated, modern parents, who are intelligent but also egoistic. Your ego is bigger than your emotions towards your wards. That's why no one was beside the child to support him when he was in depression. What option would the poor child have?)"

Sheetal grew angry and as she was opening her mouth to respond to the inspector, a nurse opened the door of the room, and said, "The patient is gaining consciousness. Any one of you can go inside the room."

Rahul rushed into the room, past the nurse who shut the door behind him; she stood just inside the room. With eyes filled with tears, he walked towards Sachin. Sitting down on the stool kept near the bed, he took Sachin's cold, limp hand in his hands, gently kissed it.

Holding his hand, with tearful eyes and in a trembling voice, he whispered, "I'm extremely sorry, son, that because of my negligence you are in such a condition. I was not beside you during perhaps the most critical time of your life. Had I been there, I would have taken all your troubles on myself and would not have allowed you to take such a drastic step."

Sachin's eyelids fluttered. With great difficulty, he opened his eyes once and then closed it. Seeing this, the nurse stepped outside to inform the doctor. After some time, a doctor, Sheetal, Inspector Khan, Sachin's school principal and class teacher all walked into the room. Rahul was trying to wake up Sachin.

Finally, Sachin opened his eyes. Rahul wiped his tears with his shirtsleeve so that Sachin wouldn't see that his father had been crying.

"Dad," Sachin said feebly, with a small smile. "You are back."

"I'm sorry, son. I was away from you when you needed me the most. But from now on, I will always be with you, my son."

Sachin smiled and said in a very weak, barely audible voice, "Promise?"

"God Promise," Rahul kissed his hand.

The doctor requested Rahul to step aside so that he could check Sachin. Rahul got up from the stool and stood near Sheetal, who was now smiling through her tears.

The doctor carefully noted Sachin's pulse, his eyes and did other preliminary checks. He looked at the patient chart, wrote some comments, and gave some oral instructions to the nurse.

Turning towards the others, he smiled slightly and said, "Good news. He is out of danger now. He is still very weak though, so allow him to sleep as much as he can. Today he will be on saline and if he maintains the same health parameters, we will start him on a light diet from tomorrow morning."

Rahul and Sheetal folded their hands and said, "Thank you, doctor. We are really grateful to you."

As the doctor nodded and left the room, followed by the nurse, Rahul turned towards Sheetal and said, "You look tired. You probably need to catch-up with your sleep as well. Why don't you go home and take some rest?"

Shaking her head, Sheetal said, "You too have come from the airport after 24 hours of flight. You also must be tired. You go home, I'll manage."

Unexpectedly, someone spoke softly and gently from behind them.

"No one needs to remain here. I will stay beside Sachin. I'm not tired and since I had slept well last night, I'm not sleepy. I will take care of Sachin, till you come back in the evening."

This was Madhuri Desai, Sachin's class teacher. Rahul was tired and upset, so he didn't notice much, but he seemed to like the voice. It sounded like a musical bell, sweet, soft and warm. The voice had a hint of affection and command, which generally comes from someone very close, very caring.

Rahul thanked her for her gesture and left the room.

★ ★ ★

After reaching home, Rahul bathed, and forced himself to eat something. He tried to sleep but could not do so, because of anxiety and worry; although Sachin was out of danger, he still could not get over the acute pain and helplessness that he was feeling. After a few unsuccessful attempts, Rahul got up and started to get ready to go to the hospital.

When he reached the hospital, it was around 1.30pm. He took the elevator to the seventh floor, and strode towards Sachin's room, quietly opened the door and peeped in. His eyes first went towards Sachin – he was fast asleep. Then he looked around to see Madhuri taking a nap. A half-open book lay in her hands, which were resting on her stomach. Rahul carefully closed the door, so as not to disturb either of them. He looked around the corridor, and seeing a row of steel chairs, sat down on one of these.

He closed his eyes. A stream of thoughts surfaced in his mind, starting from his courtship days with Sheetal; her father's objection to their relationship because of Rahul's economic background; their marriage; Rahul's struggle to get a foothold in the tough city of Mumbai; Sachin's birth; differences over career decisions vs taking care of their baby and Sheetal prioritizing her career; Rahul's anger and objection to this decision; her decision to part ways; Sachin's loneliness due to his mother's sudden exit from his life; Rahul's failed efforts to fill the void created by Sheetal; his appointment in Gold Star Electronics and busy schedule that grew hectic by the day... which got him fame and money but drastically reduced the time he used to spend with Sachin.

The more Rahul thought about Sachin, the guiltier he felt, the worse he felt. That guilt started coming out in the form of warm tears from his eyes. He didn't know how long he sat like that, his eyes closed but tears rolling down his cheeks, till a sweet and soft voice broke through his pensiveness.

"First time I'm seeing someone crying after learning that all his problems are over."

He opened his eyes. Madhuri was standing in front of him, two paper cups of coffee in her hand.

Smiling, she asked, "Coffee?"

Rahul felt himself smiling back at her, her friendly behaviour easing the tension in him.

"Do you generally drink two cups of coffee at a time?" he couldn't help asking her.

"No."

45

"That means, obviously, the second one is for me? If it is so, then why ask?" quipped Rahul.

'The guy is sharp,' flashed through Madhuri's mind, and she smiled, acknowledging it, extending one cup towards him.

Rahul took the cup of coffee, and said, "Thanks for your support. You see, I could never envisage that my son would be in such a condition. Suicide? I can't believe it even now that Sachin could take such a step. I'm just trying to reconcile with the fact."

Sitting down beside him, Madhuri said, "I can understand your feelings. But we must take solace from the fact that he is out of danger now and soon he will be with you and your family."

As she was talking to Rahul, someone waved at her, some distance away.

She waved back, and told Rahul, "My friend is there. If you don't mind, I will come in some time, say around 10 minutes? Some time back, Principal Sir had called me to say that he was planning a visit here, to see Sachin."

Rahul replied, "Sure. I will just see how Sachin is doing."

Once again he went to Sachin's room, and peeped in. Sachin was awake and gazing at the ceiling. Rahul entered the room, shutting the door quietly behind him.

"Hi! How are you, young man?"

"Hi Dad! Your young man is lying on a hospital bed."

Rahul hadn't expected Sachin to come to the topic so fast. He thought Sachin coming straight to the situation at hand indicated that something indeed was troubling him, and he was eager to discuss his problems.

Feeling that there was no point in losing time as Sachin's life was at stake, Rahul sat down at the foot of the bed and asked him, "What happened? Why did you take such a step?"

"I am bad at studies, Dad. Everyone around me is angry and unhappy with me. Mum, Principal Sir, Madhuri Ma'am... they are all unhappy with my performance. From next month, prelims are starting in school, and this time, too, I may not perform well, so again I will dishearten them. I thought, let me not disappoint them again, so I decided to end my life as I can never be a bright student in my life."

Pained at hearing this, Rahul said, "No, son, who said you are not a good student? You are a very lovely child; we all love you very much."

"That may be true, but that does not get me the marks that Mum and Principal Sir want me to get in exams. What is the use of such a dumb life? It's better to end such a life!"

Rahul could not believe that his sweet-natured son had attempted to give up his life for such a reason – because of the high expectations that people had from Sachin, on the academic front. He could not control his anguish and started sobbing for some time, holding Sachin's right hand in both his hands. Rahul couldn't help but think, how much trauma this boy has gone through just to fulfil the wishes of the elders around him.

Just then, while Rahul was trying to cheer up and assure Sachin, there was a knock on the door, and Sachin looked in that direction. Rahul also looked back and noticed people coming in but he preferred to continue talking with Sachin.

Rahul had still not come out of his state of shock and grief. That was evident from the fact that he preferred speaking to Sachin although Sheetal and Principal Roshan Daruwala had just entered the room. Sachin shyly smiled at his mum and Principal Sir; they stood a few feet away, and listened to the father–son dialogue.

Rahul continued to assure him, referring to what Sachin had just said.

"My son, this is not true. Performance in academics do give you hope for a better life, but it is not a pre-condition to success. I can count so many, highly successful and great people who have achieved amazing heights in their lives but they were not bright students. To become successful in life, it is advisable to study well, but it is certainly not essential to pass every exam with top marks!"

And Rahul solemnly declared, "From now onwards, my son, you needn't become tensed and stressed because of your exams; from now onwards your academic performance will be my responsibility. I am freeing you from my expectations and declaring to the whole world that…

It's okay to fail, my son."

Roshan Daruwala was stunned with Rahul's announcement. He found it unusual, unheard of and perhaps unacceptable, but he attributed it to Rahul's disturbed mind. He took a deep breath, and slowly walked out of the room.

It's Okay to Fail, My Son

SHEETAL WAS DUMBFOUNDED, and practically stomped out of Sachin's room. Furious, she didn't know what to do, so she sat on a chair kept in a private corridor attached to the room. She was fuming: how could Rahul take such a stand with Sachin? 'Sachin, anyway, is a hopeless case; as it is, he didn't study seriously for his exams, and now, after such an announcement from his dad, he wouldn't study at all! If he didn't study, what sort of life would he lead in today's competitive world? Will he beg or steal?' she grumbled within.

Suddenly she saw Rahul walking towards her. She got into a combative posture, as if a cat was about to pounce on its prey.

Rahul had glanced around, and seeing Sheetal, had come towards her, smiling.

"Coffee?" he asked.

"No, give me poison instead," replied Sheetal, bitterly.

Rahul was still in a light mood, and appeared to be putting in a lot of effort to make Sheetal smile. But Sheetal was determined to be hostile. Rahul went near the coffee machine and returned with two cups of coffee.

Sheetal could not control herself any longer, and burst out anxiously, the moment Rahul came near her.

"What did you say? It's okay to fail? It's okay to fail! How can you be so irresponsible, Rahul, with our own child? Why do you want him to fail in his studies? What will he do for his future, Rahul?" her eyes were brimming with tears.

Rahul offered her coffee, saying firmly but gently, "One thing at a time, first enjoy your coffee."

"Enjoy the coffee? I am dying and you are asking me to enjoy? Are you in your senses?" she was about to blast.

"Okay, let me explain. I told him 'it's okay to fail', only to remove the fear of failure from his mind. Due to this pressure, we could have lost our child, Sheetal, it's because of someone's blessings on us that he is alive today. Studies are a necessity, I agree with you, but it is not everything and certainly not above the life of our child. Besides, why are you worried? He will excel in life, that's my promise to you."

Rahul paused for some time, thinking. Then he continued, "What I need from you is your support and cooperation. He is our child. He is our dream and future. Please be with me, we will do everything possible to offer him a good life and career."

"But how? I have my practice; you have taken up a new assignment, who will attend to him?"

"I will attend to him, I will do everything possible in this world for Sachin. He will excel in his studies, and in whatever he wants to do or aspires for in his life. It is just a question of mindset. I will change his mindset, I will make him tough – like Vivekananda who remembered every page of the book that he read even just once. Like Thomas Alva Edison, who considered every failure as a new learning! I will prepare him to aim at excellence in all spheres of life," Rahul's face glowed with confidence and determination.

Sheetal seemed to be in dilemma; she didn't know how to react. For the first time after so many years, she remained silent in an argument. She looked at Rahul as if she had met him for the first time.

★   ★   ★

Then, for nearly a fortnight, till the time Sachin was in hospital, Rahul attended to him.

One evening, when they were together, Sachin asked him, "Dad, do you love me?"

"My son, what a silly question! Of course, I love you – a lot."

"Then why do you spend so much time outside, leaving me alone at home? You know how lonely I feel when you are not with me. I get really scared."

"Son, like every other father in this world, I too work for your future. I wish to work so hard that I can give you and your mum all the comforts of life. You don't have to struggle for the things that I had to struggle for during my childhood. Sachin, our community is highly misunderstood."

"Community? Dad, you belong to a community? Why didn't I know about it?" asked Sachin, surprised.

"I belong to the community of fathers, which is highly misunderstood. You see, the whole world, including poets and authors, have put in millions of pages on mothers. But, no one has written anything on us, fathers," Rahul said, pretending to be complaining to Sachin.

Sachin said innocently, "Don't worry, Dad. I will write a book on you and all fathers of the world."

Rahul smiled, "That would be very sweet of you, my son."

Picking up the thread from his earlier conversation, Rahul said, "Your grandfather, that is, my father, was a poor assistant in a municipal school. We were four siblings. We lived in a small house, in a small chawl in central Mumbai, much smaller than any of the bathrooms we have in our house today. His income was not enough to even feed our family, forget about the other comforts of life.

"From my childhood, I have been fond of studies. But we did not have money to even buy books. Still, life was good, we had a peaceful and joyful life, but one day things changed dramatically. I was returning home from school, when Irfan Uncle, our neighbour, asked me to rush home as there was some tension at home. When I reached home, everyone in my family was crying. As I was quite young at that time, I didn't understand what was happening.

"I asked our next-door neighbour – I called her Aunty – and she said Father had had a paralytic attack. I asked my elder sister, your Saumya Aunty, what that meant, and she said that Dad was in a hospital and he would not be able to walk ever again. I still didn't realize the gravity of that incident till it really started to affect us.

"After that incident, the next few years were very difficult for all of us. Father was bedridden, his salary had stopped, and we were living on his pension, which was a meagre amount. Of course, the school authorities were kind and they did try to help our family, but that was not enough. Your grandmother had taken up washing utensils and other household chores of other families to make both ends meet, but during the last few days of the month, the whole family – except me – would go without food.

"Years passed by, I stood first in the whole school in SSC. Then I did my engineering, with financial help from others. I remember I needed a dissection box in Class XII, and my mother did not have even ₹55 for the same. So, Mother took me to a nearby charitable foundation along with my mark sheet, seeking help. They saw my mark sheet, overall performance and promised to support my studies.

"We were all passing through a difficult time. The year in which I passed my engineering… Dad passed away."

Rahul folded his hands and closed his eyes as if he was paying tribute to his father. Sachin reached out to the table kept next to his bed, picked up the water bottle, opened its lid and handed the bottle to Rahul.

Rahul drank some water and continued, "Mother and my sisters shouldered my responsibility and supported my studies. During my childhood, I didn't know what luxury meant! What is available to you today so readily and easily, were unheard of in my childhood.

"Since I suffered mostly during my childhood, as a father I always prayed that you should never suffer. Now this is not unique to me, every responsible father thinks like this. This feeling of giving extra safety, comfort and happiness to you inspires me to work hard. You need to understand that I, too, have my likings and dislikings. I too need to rest. I too feel like socializing, to go on a long vacation with you and Mum. Live life like other dads and husbands, but it is your well-being, your future, which takes priority over my likings. That is the reason why I work so hard."

Sachin's eyes were filled with gratitude. Lying on his bed, he stretched out his hands and gestured Rahul to embrace him.

"I'm sorry, Dad, I misunderstood you, I always used to think that you didn't care for me. Even Mum thinks that way. But now I understand the reason behind your working so hard, staying away from us is a big sacrifice that you are making for us.

"Despite Mum's and my strong resistance, you have continued working so hard. Now I realize that you did all this to make my future safe and secured. I wish I had understood it before. I promise not to repeat such mistakes, and obey you and work towards fulfilling your dreams for me and our family."

His statement, full of assurance and understanding, relieved Rahul. Both father and son gave each other a tight hug like never before. Time stopped, as if it were never to witness such bonding ever again.

The Big Decision

'IT'S DIFFERENT TODAY, strange things are happening since morning,' Madhuri thought. 'The milkman left four pouches instead of the usual two; the newspaper vendor gave us a Gujarati paper, when we don't subscribe to it... I don't even know Gujarati!'

"It's a strange day today," she murmured to herself as she walked through the main gate of the school, Shri Saraswati Vidhya Mandir.

Suddenly, a brand-new red-coloured Lamborghini Veneno vroomed past her.

'Such an expensive car in our school,' she mused, 'must belong to some parent.'

She walked towards the administrative office – which was located next to the principal's office – to mark her attendance, and saw the same car parked outside the principal's office. She walked into the office next to the principal's, where the attendance muster was kept. The principal's office door was slightly ajar. She couldn't believe her eyes, when she saw who was sitting with Principal Roshan Daruwala. It was Rahul! Snatches of their conversation came to her ears as she opened the heavy attendance muster, and filled in the details. Curiosity getting the better of her, she took her time to sign-in that morning. She overheard a bit of the discussion, and paused a while.

The principal was saying, "No, Mr Saxena, it is not possible. We cannot allow you to experiment with the lives of so many students. I empathize with you: you are passing through a difficult stage of your life. I suggest you take it easy, spend some time with your family... with Sachin... and everything will be normal in a few weeks' time. You can even plan a short vacation in India or abroad. Really, you don't need to worry about Sachin's future, we are there to take care of him. He is a good student, he will do well. This is just a phase, it will pass."

Principal Roshan Daruwala was frantically trying to pursue his point with Rahul, who spoke calmly.

"No, sir, it is not an emotional decision. I have given this particular matter a great deal of thought and only then did I come to this conclusion. As a matter of fact, I have already acted on my decision. I have already resigned from my job, the post of CEO of Gold Star Electronics. Sir, I have resigned at a time when they offered me a global role and board member in the USA. This in itself shows how very serious I am about my decision."

Taken aback as she herself was, Madhuri could make out from the principal's voice how shocked he was at Rahul's resignation.

"What? You have resigned from your job? It's crazy. The kind of job, which is the dream of every professional in the Indian electronics industry, you have given up because of your decision? I can't believe it. Why should you give up such a high-paying job? What for? *Arrey*, the kind of money you are getting right now, your son need not do anything in his entire life!"

"Yes. You are right," agreed Rahul quietly, "I earn so much that I can leave a sufficient amount for my son to lead a comfortable life. But I won't do that because I don't want my son to become a lazy idiot. Like every loving father, I want him to excel in everything he does, or aspires to do in life. Money is not everything, it's talent, knowledge and passion that differentiates a genius and an ordinary man. I want him to be a genius and that is precisely the reason why I have taken this decision."

Madhuri could pick up only that much from the conversation between Rahul and Principal Sir. But she really couldn't make out what the disagreement was about, what decision had Rahul taken that Principal Sir was objecting to so vehemently?

As the school bell rang, signifying the beginning of classes that day, Madhuri left the attendance muster room, and started walking towards her class wondering what that decision was!

★　★　★

"Good morning, ma'am," greeted her students, as Madhuri entered the class.

"Good morning," she replied, seemingly lost in her thoughts.

But her eyes were wandering as if they were looking for someone. Finally, her eyes rested on the one boy she was seeking in the class.

"Samir, how are you?" she asked one of the boys.

Samir was a close friend of Sachin's.

"Good morning, ma'am," responded Samir, surprised at being singled out thus. "I am fine, ma'am."

"Have you met Sachin recently?"

"No, ma'am."

"Oh, I see."

"Anything urgent, ma'am?"

"No, it's alright," Madhuri nodded her thanks, and Samir sat down, wondering what it was all about.

*   *   *

Class over, as Madhuri was walking out of the class room, the principal's voice rang out on the speakers of the public announcement system.

"All school committee members are requested to come to the conference room adjacent to my office in the lunch recess."

Madhuri was one of the committee members, and it was lunchtime. 'Oh dear, I will miss my lunch today,' was the very first thought that surfaced in Madhuri's mind.

"I missed my breakfast too in the morning!" she murmured to herself.

Standing at some distance was the Lamborghini, Madhuri noticed. It was still parked outside the block that housed the principal's office.

When she was near the venue, she saw an office boy who had just walked out of the conference room. He informed her that all committee members had already gathered there. She hurried in, and took a seat. As she saw them, the qualities and anecdotes associated with each teacher flashed through her mind. Mr Meenakshi, the IT teacher, who was known as the 'walking-talking computer'. Meenakshi had a weird habit of interfering in other people's matters.

Mr Bhattacharya, the maths teacher, was a very strict teacher. Famous among students for his harsh imposition of self-defined behaviour, it was rumoured among students that if Bhattacharya finds you on the wrong side, he would first give a slap and then inform why he had given the slap! Bhattacharya had been warned several times by Principal Roshan Daruwala, but to no avail. He was one of the oldest and seniormost teachers in school, so even Principal Sir gave him a bit of flexibility. Students called him 'Hitler' behind his back because of his strictness.

Mr Khan taught science; he had just returned from the US. In spite of many job offers from the private sector, he chose the teaching profession over big sums of money. He was known to be the most loving and caring teacher in the school and also known for his straightforward attitude.

Mr Batliwala, the chairman of the school, hailed from a Parsi family that was known for their wealth and nobility. His grandfather had built Saraswati Vidhya Mandir in 1950.

Then, Madhuri's eyes fell on Mr Pratap Dikshit, a local politician and school trustee. Due to his high-handed, abusive behaviour, his surname had been broken into two parts: 'Dick's Shit'. Just recently, a scandal involving him in a land-grabbing instance had been exposed by the media. The land, which belonged to poor families, had been grabbed by his party and given to affluent builders in Mumbai. But as usual, he was shameless. He had a habit of staring at all lady staff members, so all the ladies in the staff generally preferred to stay away from him, as far as possible. Madhuri also had a feeling that Dikshit had an eye on her but she couldn't care less. Seeing her looking at him, he smiled and waved at Madhuri, but she acted as if she hadn't seen him at all! And, to Madhuri's surprise, Rahul too was there. Sitting next to the principal.

As Madhuri settled down on her seat, Principal Daruwala got up from his chair and addressed the little gathering in the conference room.

"I'm sorry to call all of you at such a short notice and that too during lunchtime. But don't worry, I have organized a nice working lunch for all of us. So we can have lunch and the meeting too. We can manage both.

"I'm facing a dilemma which I thought I should discuss with you all and take your opinion to arrive at a decision, which will be in the best interest of our school and its students."

He paused for some time and looked at Rahul with a smile, "I am privileged to have with us today the very famous and successful CEO of Gold Star Electronics, Rahul Saxena. On behalf of all of you, I welcome him and thank him, that he has found time to meet all of us. He wants to share some of his thoughts with all of you, which he has already shared with me this morning. Over to you, Rahul."

"Thanks, sir. I'm honoured with your love and affection. Actually it's my love for my son, Sachin – and why only Sachin but for every child studying in this school – that has brought me to you. I want to be given a chance to be one of you... that is, I want to teach in your school," Rahul paused as if he wanted to see the reaction of all those present.

Everyone, except the principal, was stunned.

"What?" they all exclaimed except the principal who was keenly observing them all.

"How is it possible? You are the CEO of such a big company, how can you do this ordinary job of a teacher?" Meenakshi wanted to know.

"Teaching is not a joke. How is it that you have suddenly become interested in teaching? What is the guarantee that you will stick to this honorable profession for even two months? Dealing with children is not easy, Mr Rahul. I guarantee you that you will give up," said Bhattacharya emphatically, with a big frown on his face.

Mr Batliwala too chipped in, speaking slowly and gently, "Dear son, Rahul, your plan of taking up the teaching profession is very noble. There is no profession as noble as teaching in this world! Being a parent you carve out the lives of your own children. Perhaps one or two. A doctor too saves lives but as a teacher, you influence the lives of hundreds of students... who are like tender saplings, who are not able to support themselves, who need constant support, guidance and care to acquire those competencies and skills that will enable them to face the world. But, you need to understand the fact that, while this profession gives you a lot of scope and opportunity to influence so many lives, it is disastrously low paying. Most of the teachers who are the sole bread earners of their families can't even afford their own house, forget anything else."

He looked around, most heads nodding in agreement to what he had just said. Mr Batliwala continued, "Particularly for you, who has such a highly paid and glamorous job. If you don't mind, can you tell us, how much salary are you drawing?"

Rahul hesitated for some time as he was not comfortable discussing his salary package in front of so many people. However, since the question had come from the chairman of the school, he didn't have any choice.

He said, "US$ 10 mn per annum."

Everyone gasped. Instinctively, they started to convert that figure, mentally, to its equivalent in Indian rupee.

US$ 10 mn per annum means around ₹60–65 crore per annum... that means ₹5 crore a month!

As they started arriving at the astounding figure, their eyes widened, jaws almost dropping to the ground!

Politician Dikshit got up from his seat.

"Brother Rahul, your idea to leave aside such a huge salary in dollars and teach the children in our school is not convincing. This is a fleeting desire; we can't really allow you to play with the lives of so many of our students. We are not short of teachers, we too have many competent and brilliant teachers... like Madhuri Ma'am," and then looking at Madhuri, he sought confirmation, "what do you say Madhuri... Ma'am?"

Madhuri just looked at him and turned her face away.

The science teacher, Mr Khan broke in, his soft, cultured voice a contrast to the grating words of the politician.

"Rahul, it is wonderful to have a genius like you amongst us. Not only students, even we adults will be able to learn so many new things from you. I sincerely hope I'm not offending anyone when I say that none of us in this school are as learned, as travelled and as experienced as you are. Today, you have reached such a position that you have made all of us proud! Your joining our school would make us even more proud. What you have done to the business world, your company, if you do even 10 per cent of that for this school and the teaching community, I'm sure it would transform the way we teach students and the way students study!"

Madhuri was observing Rahul, who was patiently listening to the comments. She was surprised with his amazing display of perseverance and listening skills. He was silent, composed and relaxed. She thought, 'with so many comments and even criticism about his intent, an ordinary person would have started to defend himself, but Rahul seems to be in no hurry.'

When the committee members settled down, and finally turned to him, Rahul smiled and asked, "Is that all what you have to say? Does anyone else have anything else to add?"

When no one spoke, he smiled and said, "I appreciate your queries, concerns and anxieties, it is very natural for you to think what you have expressed. We all live in our own world of perceptions, mostly judging people and the phenomena around us with the yard stick of our perceived values. Based on these perceptions, often we end up labelling both people and phenomena as right or wrong. But there is nothing like right or wrong!

"How many of you believe a child will have a very bright future if he does very well in academics?"

Almost everyone in the room, except Principal Roshan Daruwala, raised their hands; Bhattacharya and Meenakshi raised both hands.

Rahul's smile broadened, as he saw the two raised hands of these two teachers, and he quipped, looking at Meenakshi, "Do you mean to say you believe it more emphatically?"

Meenakshi nodded in affirmation.

Rahul continued, "I would say, I beg to differ! It is wonderful to get educated. Education gives certain benefits which no wealth in the world can give us, because it helps to train our brain – and the mind – and makes us aware of our past history, people and the cultures around us. It helps us learn economics, human psychology, architecture and so many different subjects in an organized way. But still, we have so many people who have achieved exemplary success in their respective fields like Einstein and Thomas Alva Edison in science, and, more recently, Bill Gates in computer software and Steve Jobs too, who founded Apple. Some of them were not considered 'good' in academics and did not even complete their graduation, and a few even dropped out of college! But they did exceedingly well in their own spheres of activities. They all achieved great heights and earned name and fame for themselves."

He paused for some time, looked around and resumed, "Now look at the picture around us. How many students pass the SSC exam from this school every year? At least 300? For how many years has this school been in existence… 65 years, right? Since the school was set-up in 1950. So, that means, so far, by a rough estimate, 19,500 children have passed from this school and I'm assuming all of them must have graduated at least! Right?" He looked at all members in the room. Some of them nodded.

Rahul continued, "Now just count, in all these years, how many great personalities of the level of Newton or Einstein or Bill Gates or Steve Jobs have we created? How many of them have made it to the top league in the world?"

There was silence among the members, no one had an answer to Rahul's question.

"I want to join your school to create history, create students who are not mark-churners but experts in what they do, create history in the world of science and technology, literature, music, economics or even sports. I want your permission to be a part of this school. Please give me a chance to be one of you and together we can redefine the way students study and learn; redefine the ways teachers impart knowledge – and, more than anything else, completely redefine the way learning is being used by children to change the world around us!

"As a matter of fact, it's not only Sachin but every other child who is studying in this school, in our city, in our country and in the world around us that deserves new and perhaps better ways of learning and applying knowledge. I would like to be given a chance to teach this new way. I would like to be given a chance to learn and unlearn with all of you."

Madhuri got up from her chair and started clapping. She was supported by Principal Roshan Daruwala and Mr Khan. But Mr Bhattacharya, Mr Meenakshi and Politician Dikshit remained non-responsive.

Finally, Trustee Batliwala, the chairman, got up from his seat and came near Rahul, and putting a hand affectionately on Rahul's shoulder, said, "My dear friend, Rahul, I see a bright spark, the honesty of a child and a high amount of sincerity in your thoughts and words. We are all aware of your brilliance in science and technology as well as your management style which has contributed to the growth of your company. On behalf of my colleagues and the management committee of this school, I welcome you as an honorary member of the teaching faculty of our school. I have no doubt that your contributions will take our school to new heights and benefit the students, not only from our school alone but the whole community, the most."

The Start of a Journey

NEXT MORNING, AS Madhuri entered the gates of the school, the red-coloured Lamborghini Veneno stopped in front of her.

"Good morning, ma'am!" shouted someone from the car.

It was Sachin. He got down from the car and came near her, beaming.

"Good morning, Sachin. You're looking very cheerful, what's the matter?"

Sachin was very excited.

"Ma'am, do you know my dad is joining our school? He's going to be with me all the time. I'm so happy!" he exclaimed, grinning from ear to ear.

By then, Rahul had parked the car and had walked up to them.

"Good morning, ma'am," Rahul greeted her politely.

"Good morning! My name is Madhuri. You can call me by my name."

All three walked along as they spoke, but when Sachin saw Samir, he rushed off to greet his friend, waving goodbye to his father. Rahul waved back.

Rahul looked at Madhuri and picked up the thread of their conversation, "Sure, thank you."

Soon, they came to where Rahul had parked his car. Rahul noticed that she was looking at the car with a strange expression on her face.

Wondering about it, Rahul asked her, "Is there something troubling you? Is there something that you'd like to say?"

Madhuri replied politely, "No," and then, as though she had reached a decision after mulling over something, finally asked, "may I ask something if you don't mind?"

"Yes, you can. But just a few moments back, when I asked you the same question, your response was in the negative."

Madhuri seemed to be engrossed in her thoughts, so she ignored Rahul's comment.

Still staring at the car, Madhuri remarked, "Nice car."

"Thanks for the compliment."

"Will you get it to school every day?"

Now it was Rahul's turn to get surprised.

"Yes, but why are you asking?"

"If you don't mind… how much did this car cost?"

"Not much," Rahul shrugged. "Around ₹6 crore."

"Six crores…. That is even higher than the salary budget of the whole school for the next five years. Can I say something?"

Rahul nodded his head, wondering where this conversation was leading.

Madhuri said, choosing her words carefully, "You see, we teach lessons of simplicity and cost-saving to our students. If their one wealthy teacher comes to school every day in such an expensive car, just think of the students and the other teachers in the school, who can't even afford an auto rickshaw on a daily basis. Don't you think it can set a wrong example to them? They will never feel equal to you and Sachin."

"I get your point. Do you think a bike will be alright?"

Madhuri smiled, surprised at his flexible, humble nature, "May be yes."

*   *   *

The next morning, around the same time, as Madhuri was walking through the school gate, again Sachin called out to her from behind.

This time, the father–son duo was on a bike. Rahul parked the bike and came near Madhuri.

"Does this bike look okay?"

"What make is this?"

"Honda."

"This must be expensive, too?"

"Around US\$ 50,000, that is, the current market price will be ₹30 lakh. Not much."

Nonplussed, Madhuri asked, "Can you not think or do something that is ordinary? Which can be done and understood by ordinary people? You own a car that costs ₹6 crore, a bike that costs ₹30 lakh!"

"You are right, Madhuri. In your company, I will learn to behave like an ordinary person. Please accept my new role as a teacher," Rahul smiled good-naturedly.

His frank response and acceptance without putting forward any argument touched Madhuri. She too responded with an open laugh.

*   *   *

The school bell rang. Rahul reached his class, Section A of Class IX. Besides being the class teacher of this class, Rahul would be teaching students of other sections of Class IX and all sections of Class X.

68

As he entered the class, the students stood up and greeted him, "Good morning, sir!"

"Good morning, children! My name is Rahul Saxena and I am your new class teacher. From today onwards, I'm going to help you learn new, exciting and interesting things.

"Let's begin by introducing ourselves, shall we? So let's start with myself. As you know, my name is Rahul Saxena. This is my first teaching assignment."

"Oh, then we are all sure to fail this year," groaned someone from the back of the class.

"Not really. By the way, who is that?" Rahul asked, without losing his cool.

"Sir, it is Vivek."

"No, sir, it's not me... it's Kaushik!"

Rahul looked at both Vivek and Kaushik. He gestured at the students, and said, "Could you both come here, please?"

There was pin drop silence in the class. Now they've had it, was the thought that ran through the minds of most of the students.

Vivek and Kaushik hesitantly moved towards Rahul, still protesting, "Sir, I did not say it. Sir...."

"Don't worry, I'll not punish you. Actually, I appreciate your courage to express yourself, your doubt and concerns. As your teacher, I shall take care of your fears and doubts. It's okay to express yourself. But tell me, why do you think I will fail you?"

Vivek was still hesitant to speak, and still maintained, "I didn't say it, it was Kaushik..."

But Kaushik gathered some courage and said, "Sir, I feel so because this is your first job and you have no experience in teaching students. So how will you teach us? By the time you will learn to teach, we will be facing our exams, and we may not be well-prepared for our exams."

"Vivek and Kaushik, I appreciate your concerns and promise you that you will not fail because of me. As a matter of fact, I will help you realize the highest potential that you already have in you!"

He asked the two boys to take their seats. Then, looking at the whole class, he said, "Tomorrow is Saturday. Let's play cricket in the school playground. How about it?"

There was silence for some time, and then the students realized that it was a teacher who was proposing a game of cricket, so, why not? The next moment, there was a loud unanimous response from almost all students.

"Yes, sir!"

"Okay, I will get my cricket kit. Our school starts at eight in the morning, so can you all come at seven then?"

Then, for the next 20 minutes, Rahul discussed cricket with the class. He noticed how much the students loved to play cricket; the subject of cricket had caught the fancy of most students. No one realized how quickly time passed, and the bell rang announcing the end of this particular class and the beginning of the next.

The whole class looked invigorated, as if they had been re-energized. They were excited about cricket, and that too playing with a teacher.

The next period was with Mr Bhattacharya. As he entered the class, he was furious to see the children talking amongst themselves loudly and animatedly; it seemed as though no one had noticed him!

He banged the duster on the desk and shouted, "What is this all?! Is this the fish market?!"

Expectedly, there was pin drop silence in the class.

★　　★　　★

The next morning, as the principal entered the school at around 7.15am, he was surprised to see children, so early in the day, playing cricket in the school playground. He slowly walked towards the gallery where Rahul was sitting and watching the game.

Seeing the principal, Rahul stood up and greeted him, "Good morning, sir."

"Good morning, Rahul. Nice... you have given these children an opportunity to play and also relax."

A big roar on the ground caught their attention. The fielding team was making a racket, appealing to the umpire, who had not yet responded.

Then, the batsman – Sachin – against whom they had appealed, got into the argument, protesting, "I'm not out. My bat didn't touch the ball."

After a while, at the umpire's intervention, the boys resumed their game, and one more ball to the batsman and lo! The batsman was bowled out. All the fielders got together, excited, and started dancing with joy. Suddenly, some boys rushed towards Rahul and asked him to bat. Rahul refused, but when the children insisted, he had no option but to agree. Rahul took the bat and walked to the crease.

By this time, other teachers had arrived, including Madhuri. Rahul went on the crease and took his position; the bowler took a long run and bowled at Rahul. With every intention of hitting a boundary, Rahul swung the bat in the air, but it was an off-spin ball, and he was unable to read the ball correctly. There was a thud from behind – the bails on the stumps flew into the air, before resting on the ground. Rahul was clean bowled!

The whole ground was stunned into silence. Initially, for a few minutes, Rahul was disappointed with his own performance, but soon took charge of his emotions. And then walked towards the bowler, Samir.

"Oh-oh, big trouble for Samir," muttered Kaushik.

As Samir saw Rahul coming towards him, he realized he had badly blundered by throwing a spinner at the new teacher.

Soon, Samir saw Rahul standing in front of him with an extended hand; he closed his eyes murmuring, "Sorry, sir, sorry, sir."

Everyone on the ground thought Samir would now get a slap on his face… everyone on the ground grew tensed… Principal Sir, Madhuri, Bhattacharya, Meenakshi, Sachin, Kaushik, office boys. Every eye had the same question: what will happen next?

Samir felt a gentle hand on his head.

"Great, Samir, congratulations! That was an excellent delivery! You stumped Sachin and even me in the first ball… ha ha ha!" and he laughed heartily.

Samir slowly opened his eyes, still looking at Rahul in disbelief. Those on the ground were surprised to see Rahul's reaction. Accepting defeat wholeheartedly and that too from a student! Everyone on the ground clapped, apparently for Samir, but somewhere Madhuri felt the applause should be for Rahul, who was not at all perturbed by the incident, as if for him success and failure were two sides of the same coin, to be accepted with grace.

'Perhaps yes,' she thought.

★　★　★

That evening, Rahul and Sachin were out for a walk. Sachin looked puzzled, so Rahul asked him about it.

"What's bothering you, son? You look puzzled."

72

"Yes, Dad, I am."

"Tell me, I might be able to help you."

"Yes, you only can answer it. Today, when Samir clean bowled you, you did not get angry or disturbed. Instead, you patted him on his back, congratulated him. If it were any other teacher in school, he would have felt insulted and reacted to Samir in some other way. But you behaved differently than any other teacher in school!"

Rahul smiled and said, "You see, son. All of us want to excel in life. But to achieve excellence, one must develop the first and basic capability: the capability to fail. And more than that, one must accept his failure with grace. Because whenever you take up anything new, you are going to face several challenges, which, perhaps, you had not thought of or envisaged. For example, in cricket, when you are batting, you face several types of balls such as off spin, leg spin, bouncer, mid pitch, etc. Now, the technique for playing each ball is different. When you face these balls initially, you may not know all those techniques and so you may fail when facing them. That is exactly what happened with me today. I was clean bowled! But it doesn't prove that I am a poor or weak batsman; it only proves that I still have not mastered the art of facing spin balls!

"One incident does not make anyone a success or a failure, it just indicates the need for more learning, more practice. Now it depends on you, how you take this failure, as part of your journey towards success and excellence or do you take it to heart and give up trying, feeling disappointed and ashamed that you got out in the first ball! That is your attitude towards an incident. And remember, your future is decided by your mindset and your attitude towards all the incidents that you are

73

facing, or will be facing. If your attitude is to study, analyse, learn and correct, you will come out with flying colours. But, if you choose to take every incident to heart and choose to react, you may have a feeling of winning in those moments around the incident. However, you may lose in the long run as you have missed opportunities on key aspects of studying, learning and correcting."

Rahul continued to look at Sachin and said, "If you start thinking of one failure as a failure and live with it for long, it also indicates your attitude that you want self-imagined victory every time. That may prompt you to risk averseness – you will always go by safe and proven techniques. You will stop experimenting. The moment you stop experimenting, you will be moving towards mediocrity.

"Failure is a big teacher, son, you must learn from every failure. For that, you must learn to accept failure with the same ease as you will normally accept success.

"By learning and gradually increasing your knowledge about a subject and by trying new ways of facing a challenge, you start your journey towards mastering that subject. So accepting the situation as it is, will be your first step towards mastering the subject. I want you to learn this. Remember, every incident in life teaches us something, provided we keep the doors of our mind open for it."

Sachin got into deep thought as if he listened to – and appreciated – every word of Rahul's.

The Turning Point

IT WAS BHATTACHARYA'S class – mathematics. He entered the class and started writing a sum on the board. As soon as he had written the sum, he turned back and looked at Samir.

"Come on, Samir, can you solve this sum?"

Samir looked at the sum but was not sure, so he appeared hesitant.

"Samir, you got a lot of appreciation that day on the cricket ground for your bowling; I want you to get claps for solving this sum also."

Then looking at the students, Bhattacharya asked, "Will you all clap for Samir, if he solves this sum?"

In a chorus, the students replied, "Yes, sir!"

Bhattacharya scowled at Samir, and literally ordered the frightened boy to come near the blackboard and solve the sum. Samir became even more nervous and started trembling, his eyes showed his growing helplessness and there was a hint of tears in them.

He pleaded with Bhattacharya, "I can't solve this sum, sir."

Now Bhattacharya lost his cool and started scolding Samir in his usual acerbic way, "You can play cricket and get applauded for it, you are very confident then, but when it comes to solving a maths sum, you lose all your confidence. Why, Samir, tell me, I'm asking you why? Are you not interested in studies? I'll tell you why…. You are interested only in playing games, that's the reason why you do very well in games but when it comes to studies, you give up. We teachers and parents do so much for you, now it's your turn to perform!" he barked.

Perhaps it was a coincidence, but at that very moment, Rahul was passing by this class, and when Bhattacharya saw him, he grew even more aggressive.

He abruptly called out to Rahul, "Rahulbaba, oh Rahulbaba!"

Hearing his name, Rahul stopped and looked around, and then he saw Bhattacharya staring at him.

Rahul asked politely, "Bhattacharyaji, did you call me?"

"Yes, can you come inside?"

"But I have to go for my class, can we talk after some time?"

"No, Rahulbaba, you need to know the facts. Your beloved student, whom the whole class cheered on the cricket ground the other day, can't solve even a simple sum of mathematics."

Hearing the sharp, taunting tone in his voice, Rahul was taken aback. He entered the class, saw Samir standing near the blackboard, pale and frightened.

Rahul realized Samir's mental state so he defended Samir, and said, "Please don't say that, Samir is a very smart boy, he'll be able to solve the sum, I'm sure."

"Really? Then ask him to solve this sum right now!"

Rahul glanced at the sum and then at Samir. The boy was clearly scared, and trembling in fear.

"See, Bhattacharya Sir, it wouldn't be fair to form an opinion about Samir's capabilities from one instance. May be he has not prepared for this particular sum. But that does not prove that he doesn't know mathematics. With your permission, may I check his mathematical skills?" Rahul asked Bhattacharya.

"Yes, you can. He won't solve even your sum, I know."

Rahul turned to Samir, "My friend, you don't need to be afraid. Not being able to solve one sum just proves that you haven't practised that sum or that type of sum. Tell me, which chapter have you studied well?"

"Circles in geometry, sir."

"Which part of circles?"

"Anything in circles, sir, I have prepared it thoroughly. You can ask me any question from circles, sir," Samir replied confidently.

"Okay, then solve this question."

Rahul wrote a question on the board, which Samir solved immediately.

"Great, Samir, it's correct! Children, please give a big hand to Samir."

Bhattacharya was not ready to accept this, "What nonsense is this? In exams, sums won't be given to students after checking with them if they know it or not! You don't have a choice in exams; you either know it and solve the sum to get marks and pass, or you simply don't know, don't solve and don't get marks. You fail! Rahulbaba, it's that simple, why are you twisting it?"

"I agree with you, Bhattacharyaji, that students won't get choice in exams, but you can give them choice when they are learning. There is a difference in their status; in class they are preparing and in exam, they are prepared. So imposing the 'prepared' state while 'preparing' is incorrect. By ridiculing them for their weaknesses, we do them more harm than good, and we don't even realize it. These are tender plants, they need to be nurtured, be given confidence and hope, and the right amount of motivation and guidance."

"I agree with Rahul," came a voice from near the door of the class.

It was Principal Daruwala. The entire discussion took a completely new direction with the principal's arrival on the scene. The students looked at each other, enjoying the little drama: the principal siding with Rahul, and Bhattacharya's growing annoyance!

"Students need to be given the right atmosphere, the right kind of guidance and they will do wonders. But, Bhattacharya, your style is very different. I'm not saying your style is good or bad, but you need to be flexible depending on the needs of the students or the situation. You put students under a great amount of pressure, thinking that if they are pressurized to perform better, they will put in more effort and will excel, but it may not be true all the time."

In the face of open criticism from the principal himself, Bhattacharya lost his temper.

Raising his voice, he argued fiercely, "You are challenging me? I've been in this profession for so many years and have taught so many students, no one has ever questioned me so far and, now, a few-days-old Rahul is teaching me how to teach?"

Realizing that the situation may get out of control, the principal said quietly, "Bhattacharya, let's not argue here, but Rahul has a point so I want a debate on this subject in the auditorium after classes are over."

Both Rahul and the principal left the class, and so did Bhattacharya who was clearly furious. He didn't complete the period and left the class halfway.

Within moments, it seemed, the entire school had heard of the argument between Rahul and Bhattacharya. Of course, all those who didn't know the complete story and how it had unfolded, were gossiping away merrily – perhaps they weren't interested in knowing the truth. Many of them were simply adding layers to the story!

During lunch break, Bhattacharya spoke to the teachers indignantly, "They will teach me how to teach? I have been teaching students for so many years and now I have to listen to a novice like Rahul? What a joke!"

Madhuri was present and she heard Bhattacharya's arguments. Since she felt that Rahul was right in this case, she openly supported Rahul.

"Bhattacharya Sir, he is right. We must understand Rahul and his thoughts, he has seen the world, though different, but he has a very successful background. He has new ideas which you and I may not have, so why not give him a chance!" she suggested.

Bhattacharya did not respond, but glared at her. The other teachers in the room were all with Bhattacharya, wanting to take on Rahul and his new methods that may sound appealing in theory but were impossible to put in practice.

Bhattacharya looked at Madhuri coldly and said, "Let's see what happens in the auditorium."

Madhuri didn't know how to react to such an elderly person.

*　　*　　*

The school bell rang, announcing the day was over, but no one rushed towards the school gates. Instead, teachers, students, office boys, and support staff all made their way towards the auditorium. Bhattacharya too entered the auditorium, and so did

Rahul, after some time. Bhattacharya was still in a bad mood; Rahul was silent and composed.

Murmurs and whispers filled the auditorium as the seats filled up one by one. The auditorium was divided in clusters of small groups, who were, no doubt discussing the same subject.

As Principal Sir walked towards the microphone, there was a hush in the auditorium.

"Dear friends and colleagues! The first time in my 35 years of teaching, I came across an extraordinary situation. I have been, along with all of you, teaching students in the so-called appropriate and conventional method, conducting exams year after year, passing hundreds of students – and failing many of them too.

"So far, I have been operating from the belief that I have taught students in the best way I could. Period. My job is over, now it is up to the students to perform; in the two extremes of either securing the first rank in exams, in the class or division or may be fail. And this is the way that most of you have been thinking as well, including Mr Bhattacharya."

Glancing at the teachers sitting in the front row, his eyes finally stopped at Bhattacharya, who nodded in agreement.

"But, today, I accidentally happened to be part of an argument, which I feel has shaken my very belief system. You are all aware that at our school, Saraswati Vidhya Mandir, we continuously strive towards and promote excellence in everything we do and one of the ways to find excellence is through innovation. So, I've invited a debate between my two respected colleagues, Mr Bhattacharya and Rahul, to put forward their view points and let you decide what is good for the students and school."

He looked at Bhattacharya who was still scowling. Smilingly, he added, "First, I would like to invite Mr Bhattacharya to explain the background of our debate and share his thoughts with us, after which I would also like Rahul to share his thoughts. I am sure we will have a healthy discussion rather than a personality clash."

Bhattacharya walked towards the microphone.

"Today I was teaching maths to a section of Class IX. I had asked one of the students, I think Samir, to solve a sum on the board. He could not, so I scolded him and conveyed my expectations that he must know the chapter well, once the subject or the topic has been taught in the class.

"At that time, Rahul Saxena was passing by, so I called him and complained to him that his cricket star was not able to solve a simple question given by me. Rahulbaba was very casual towards Samir's incapability to solve the question and started lecturing me on the need to nurture students, give them proper environment and whatnot.

"Tell me, if we start giving a 'personal touch' to every student, as Rahulbaba expects, when do you think I will finish my syllabus?"

Bhattacharya paused, waiting for his words to sink in. He gestured at the students, and then continued, "And these naughty children, do you think they deserve kindness and all sorts of consideration? Despite my being strict with them, they make a fool of me. I don't think they will produce anything different, I mean better results, if they were treated differently. What do you think?"

There was some hustle-bustle in the first row as almost all teachers raised their hands and responded to Bhattacharya in affirmation, except Madhuri and, of course, the principal.

With an air of achievement, Bhattacharya looked at Rahul and said, "Now it's your turn."

Looking disturbed, Rahul walked towards the microphone. He took the microphone in hand and addressed the gathering.

"My dear teacher friends, students and Principal Sir. It's unfortunate that a small incident is taking such an unpleasant and, perhaps, a dramatic turn. I have taken up the teaching profession for my own personal reasons," and then gesturing at the students sitting in the rows, added, "and for the overall well-being of all these innocent and energetic minds.

"I am neither here to compete with anyone nor to prove anyone or his style and methods wrong. But before I say anything further, I wish to conduct a small demonstration in front of all of you. May I, Principal Sir?" looking at Principal Daruwala, Rahul sought his permission.

The principal nodded, granting permission.

"Madhuri Miss…" he looked at Madhuri, who walked towards the door and beckoned someone standing outside. Four children – two boys and two girls – entered, all in the age group of 3.5-4 years, and she guided them towards the dais. As the children followed Madhuri, they looked very cute but appeared afraid and confused. They were dressed in the school uniform meant for children in KG.

As they came close to Rahul, he shook hands with each of them and asked the child standing closest to him, his name.

"What's your name, beta?"

"Samir Shashi Kant Parekh. I am studying in Saraswati Vidhya Mandir School in Sr KG. My teacher's name is Miss Falguni. I stay at Sarvonnati Society at Vile Parle. My father's name is Shashikant and my mother's name is Seema."

As Samir was introducing himself, everyone in the auditorium broke into gentle laughter. Rahul too smiled at Samir, appreciating his innocence.

"Okay, Samir, thank you."

Then he turned towards the child next in line, a girl.

"What's your name, beta?"

"Sweety Meenatai Deosthale. *Main* Mummy *ki beti hoon*. I am studying in Saraswati Vidhya Mandir School in Sr KG. My teacher's name is Miss Falguni. I stay at Gokuldham Society at Vile Parle. My father's name is Atmaram and my mother's name is Meenatai."

Laughter rippled through the auditorium once again. Rahul looked at her with a lot of love and appreciation.

Then he turned towards the next girl.

"Just tell us your name, okay?"

"My name is Shweta Kaushik Bhandarkar. I am studying in Saraswati Vidhya Mandir School in Sr KG. My teacher's name is Miss Falguni. I stay at Damodar Park at Vile Parle. My father's name is Kaushik and my mother's name is Swati."

Rahul then turned towards the fourth and last child, a boy.

"Can you introduce yourself?"

"Yes, sir. My name is Shrikant Shivaji Khandekar. I am studying in Saraswati Vidhya Mandir School in Sr KG. My teacher's name is Miss Falguni. I stay at Gemini Building at Vile Parle. My father's name is Shivaji and my mother's name is Preeti."

Most teachers looked bored; Rahul noticed it, but preferred to overlook it.

He looked at all the children and asked them, "Is your teacher present here?"

Samir pointed a finger at one young, fair girl. Rahul waved at her, and then turned his attention on the four children once again.

"What did you learn today in class?"

All the children replied, enthusiastically, "Bhim *ki kahani*. Do you know, he is so brave and strong? He can eat a lot of *laddoos* at a time, may be truck load full."

Then thinking a bit, "May be fifty or hundred."

"And then what power he has."

"He can defeat even the biggest demon with just one punch."

When Rahul asked this question, the children were very excited, and keen to tell their part of the story. In their eagerness, these little children were all speaking simultaneously, but mostly the same story, the same words, same expressions!

Madhuri asked, "Which poem did you learn?"

"Johnny, Johnny

Yes Papa,

Brush your teeth,

Yes Papa,

Eating sugar?

No Papa,

Telling lies?

Ha Ha Ha."

Rahul addressed the audience, "Look at the mood, enthusiasm and energy of these children when they are talking about their class. And, to our surprise, they remember every bit of what they have learnt in class.

"Now let's look at how they are performing in tests. May I ask Miss Falguni to come on stage and share some insights on the performance of these children?"

Falguni walked up to the stage and stood near Rahul.

"Thanks. Can you tell us about their performance in the tests you conduct?"

"Most of them score good marks, mostly 80–85 out of 100, in most subjects."

"How about their memory, are they able to recall whatever you teach them?"

"Mostly yes. They are playful and hence lack concentration, but whenever I tell them stories, they remember it completely. It has happened many times that they are so very engrossed in the story that they remember every word of it. Their memory is so good that sometimes, by chance, if I tell them the same story on two consecutive days, they will point out any change in the sequence or even in the language. Which means, if I tell them the same story differently, they will correct it according to what they have heard earlier. It is this capability of children that amazes me."

"Okay, ma'am. Thanks for your inputs. Kindly send these children to their class and please be seated."

Rahul continued, "The French emperor Napoleon Bonaparte had once said that all people are born with the same intelligence, there is nothing like anyone being dumb or a genius – and I fully agree with him. Physiologically, everyone's brain is the same when they are born, with the same memory and same capability."

He paused, to see the reaction of his audience. Most of them looked puzzled, as if they were not able to decide whether Rahul's statement was correct or not.

Bhattacharya immediately got up from his seat and said forcefully, "No, Rahulbaba, I do not agree. You have so many students in a class, of which one comes first, most pass and some even fail. If people have the same memory, the same capability, then all of them must produce similar results."

Smiling, Rahul looked at Bhattacharya and said, "I didn't complete Napoleon's quote. Let me give you the complete one: all people are born with the same intelligence, there is nothing like dumb or genius, it is one's level of interest that decides one's performance in a particular subject. The interest level is the key differentiator in why one child stands first and why another child fails though both of them are sitting in the same class.

"Can anyone of you tell me, what do we shape here for the hundreds of students who attend school every day?" Rahul questioned the gathering.

"Future," someone said from a remote corner.

"We shape their brain," replied another voice from another direction.

Rahul looked at Bhattacharya and asked, "Would you like to guess, Bhattacharya Sir?"

"We shape their behaviour, we teach them discipline."

Rahul glanced at Madhuri and asked, "Would you like to guess, ma'am?"

She remained silent for a while, before answering, "Attitude."

"All of you are partly right in your guesses, but if I have to describe it in one word, I would say 'interest' – we shape their interest in attaining knowledge. And through our day-to-day activities, we intend to do just that, but does it actually happen?" Rahul paused, sighed and said, "Unfortunately, in most cases, it doesn't happen.

"That's the reason why children who score 85–90 per cent in KG start losing out in their marks as they grow up! And by the time they are in the seventh or eighth standard, we have four categories of students: Outstanding, those who stand between the first and fifth; Clever, those who come till the tenth rank in class; Mediocre, who usually pass with average marks; and the Unfortunate lot whom we label as disinterested, incapable, incompetent, non-serious, etc.," Rahul stopped, looked around at the audience, and then resumed.

"And what happens after that is even more serious. People around these students use these labels and treat them accordingly. The outstanding and clever students get importance at the cost of the rest of the students in class."

Bhattacharya stood up and demanded loudly, raising his voice to such a pitch that it sounded like he was almost shouting at Rahul with frustration and anger, "What's wrong in that? Outstanding and clever students put that extra effort in learning and hence we like them. I don't see anything wrong in this approach!"

"Certainly, I'm not at all suggesting that the current approach is wrong, but when you have found out the reason/attributes of why clever students are so, can you share with me one reason, why poor performing students are so?"

"They are lazy and useless. They don't like to work, just attend school and waste everyone's time."

"See, a few more labels," Rahul remarked promptly. "What I can see with my little knowledge is that most of the people around weak students fail to treat them with dignity, at times even hurt their self-esteem. I wish to put forward a psychological analysis of why certain students are not able to do as desired in their academic performance. However, before that, I wish to convey some facts about all students, including the poorly performing ones: they are all equal in intelligence, and as capable as every other student in the class or school. Given a chance, even the student who has failed can achieve the highest marks in class, provided we teachers guide and rekindle his/her interest, enthusiasm and confidence on the subject.

"But despite willingness and capabilities, if the child is still not able to make it to the expected performance standards, then the reason lies with us. We are to be blamed for his incapability! I am sure if we can modify our approach and look at students with more empathy, we can make a big difference in their learning abilities, which in turn can impact their academic performance, and–"

"Stop this lecture! You are new in the teaching profession, what do you know? All these sound good but it is impossible to follow them practically. Are you suggesting that I go to every student and tell him, 'My dear, you are very intelligent and capable, please tell me how do I teach you so that your hidden intelligence and potential can be tapped? Don't worry, if you still don't do well, it's my fault, and so I should get punished'?" Bhattacharya protested loudly.

At this moment, Principal Daruwala intervened, "Bhattacharya, please do not overreact. What Rahul is talking about makes a lot of sense; you should be open to new ideas and suggestions. We must try and change the ways in which we are imparting knowledge to our students."

Despite the principal's interruption and advice, Bhattacharya looked determined to challenge every argument and, surprisingly, most senior teachers in the school seemed to agree with him. Thus, the debate seemed poised between Rahul and the principal on one side, and almost the entire teaching staff of the school on the other side.

Bhattacharya got up from his seat in excitement, and said, "Rahulbaba, if you are so confident about the theories that you have put forward, I have an idea."

While everyone gazed at Bhattacharya with puzzled eyes, Rahul remained silent, nodding at the maths teacher, who continued, "There is a saying in English that the proof of pudding is not in just seeing it, but eating it. So to see the success of your idealistic views, let's agree to a challenge. We will form two batches or groups. You take a batch of 25–30 students and I choose another batch of students. You put in your best efforts to improve the performance of students. And I will take the responsibility for the performance of students of my batch. If you succeed, their lives and my belief will change for the better. If I succeed – well, any way no one loses anything – it's status quo. And you accept defeat and give up the teaching profession and leave our school."

Rahul realized that arguments would not help in coming to a solution. He thought for some time.

Suddenly his eyes brightened, he had a broad smile on his face and said, "Okay Bhattacharya, you want me to put my head on the chopping block, I will do so. I agree to the challenge put up by you."

The whole auditorium was speechless. Some like Madhuri simply sat, their eyes widening in utter disbelief, while some muttered under their breath. Suddenly, murmurs broke out in the auditorium, everyone seemed to be talking and discussing on what had just happened. Unexpectedly, Madhuri left the auditorium. Rahul was a bit surprised at her hurried and abrupt departure. 'May be she's just remembered something more important or there's a call on her mobile,' he thought.

Principal Sir felt that the discussion was going in an undesired direction, so in order to put a stop to it all, spoke up firmly, "Rahul and Bhattacharya both have points. We need to think about their points and adopt something that will be most beneficial to the school and the students. I suggest we close our meeting here. Let me think about it. In the next 2-3 days, I will let you know what should be our next course of action."

Saying this, he left the auditorium. Rahul too walked out of the hall, and headed to the parking lot where he had parked his bike. He was surprised to see Madhuri standing near his bike.

As Rahul came close to her, he smiled and said, "Hi, you left the auditorium in a hurry. Everything alright?"

He noticed that her face was pale, and she looked rather sad and upset.

Hesitatingly, Rahul murmured, "Meeting went very well, I suppose?"

Suddenly Madhuri retorted, tears welling up in her eyes, "What well? They laid a trap and you simply walked into it easily."

"Trap? What are you talking about?"

"You are very sweet and straightforward, Rahul. But they are not. Since the day you have joined school, your teaching and working style has become more and more popular. Students have started enjoying their studies, their fear for teachers has also lessened. I've noticed that even below-average students have started taking an interest in their studies, and are getting better marks in their unit tests. Due to your success in such a short time, some people, particularly those who have been teaching here for ages, are jealous of you. That's because though they are veterans in this field, their thought process and teaching methods are outdated. They are full of distrust and envy. That is perhaps the reason why they are not able to see the success and win over students' confidence, something that you have achieved in such a short period of time."

Rahul was standing in front of her, his arms folded across his chest, listening carefully to her. His body language was relaxed yet attentive.

As she finished speaking, he moved a step closer to her and said, "Look at me. I believe you are my good friend and colleague. I'm touched by your care and warmth but there is nothing to worry about; I think your concern is unnecessary. Bhattacharya and the other teachers are all good people. They have been serving this institution for many years and have certain ways of teaching and dealing with students. Their belief system has become so routine and steadfast that they feel threatened at the very thought of changing it. Knowing this fully, I purposely accepted today's challenge."

As he spoke, his posture became like one who was alert and self-reliant, his face glowed with calm confidence, and his eyes sparkled. Madhuri was overwhelmed by his body language, his poise and his words.

Rahul continued, "When something becomes so rigid and deep-rooted, you only need to shake it from within. I am certain that I will be able to help students as well as the teaching fraternity of this school through new methods that does not consider students as marks-making machines where you put in information and they produce good marks. I want to nurture these tender plants to develop into geniuses of tomorrow. I want them to work for *excellence* in whatever they do. I want to develop so much interest in them towards their studies, sports and society that they *stop* thinking of these activities as being imposed on them; rather, they would want to work for excelling in all of them!"

He paused for breath, and carried on earnestly, "I want to change the lives of these little people. I want them to not only pass with good marks and become good employees and professionals but develop into scientists, sportsmen, academicians and innovators who will not only change their own lives but also that of all countrymen and make this world a livable place."

He now looked at her, slowly reached out, took her hands in his, and said, "Are you with me in my journey?"

At Rahul's tender touch, Madhuri became speechless; it seemed to her as if the whole world had come to a standstill. Rahul and Madhuri were unaware of two eyes at a distance that had been gazing at them for a long time.

The Challenge

THE NEXT MORNING, as Rahul walked into the school staffroom, he received a call from the principal, who wanted to see him right away. When Rahul entered his office, and greeted him, Principal Daruwala received him warmly.

"Good morning to you too, Rahul. I'm sorry I called you at such short notice, but it's very important that we talk as soon as possible."

Rahul, who had wondered at the urgency of the principal's request to meet him at the earliest, to discuss something that couldn't wait till the recess, said politely, "No issues, sir, please tell me. I'll make up the time lost with students after school hours."

The principal looked at him appreciatively, "It's really wonderful to hear someone who is so dedicated about his work and the students. I'm sure you will take care of your work."

"Yes, tell me, sir, you said you wanted to speak to me of something very important."

The principal straightened his back and sat in an attentive posture. Rahul too followed him, perhaps unconsciously.

"I'm very sorry about yesterday's episode. You were dragged into it unnecessarily. We have some teachers who consider their

93

job as a burden. Then we have another set of people who just play spoilsport and add fuel to the fire by instigating the first set of people. For no fault of yours, you got into a conflict with Bhattacharya and his supporters. Yesterday's debate, which I had intended to be educative for all of us, turned into a nasty affair, which has put you into a very difficult situation and almost forced you to take up an impossible challenge. Once again, please accept my apologies."

Principal Daruwala looked worried. Rahul smiled at him.

Leaning forward and resting his hands on the table, Rahul said, "Sir, there is nothing to worry about. I don't think I've got into any difficult situation because of yesterday's debate. You mentioned a conflict, yes we got into an argument, but for a purpose. This argument is necessary to change people's thoughts, attitude and approach towards the most important job of all: teaching. People such as Mr Bhattacharya who have been in this profession for a very long time, may demonstrate a natural tendency of pre-set thoughts, procedures and methods. They think that whatever they think, believe and do is right. Now, it is very difficult to change their belief system, unless challenged through a conflict. Conflict arouses their sensibilities and thought process psychologically, whereby they start noticing every detail of what the other party is saying, and they observe developments as they happen and notice results if they are distinctly different. So this conflict, I'm sure, will have a positive impact on all of us."

"Well, I hope so," Principal Sir still looked troubled. "I also wanted to inform you about one more important point. The promoter, Shri Ratan J. Batliwala, who built this school, had a dream of education for all. So he made provision for educating children from downtrodden families in our society in the same environment and in the same fashion as the child of a rich and affluent person. We have some boys in our school who work at night as a hotel boy or a cleaner in a garage. Some of these boys are very good in terms of their behaviour, track record, etc, but they're unable to meet our standards. Last year, we had to ask two boys to leave school as they had failed in Class VIII for three consecutive years. Our school rules do not allow us to continue with such students. This year too we have three such students; one of them, Shankar, is on borderline, he has failed twice. I had called over his parents. His mother is a housemaid and the father is a drunkard. He forces the child to work at night to pay for his alcohol. I have warned him a couple of times but to no avail. Shankar is a very nice boy, but there is nothing really we can do about him. It would be good if you can do something about that child."

"Sure, sir. I will look into it."

Principal Sir continued, "By the way, how do you wish to carry forward this challenge, which was discussed yesterday with Bhattacharya? He and his political friend are very keen on my involvement, and to define the rules of the challenge."

"I'm okay... any time."

"Today... after school hours? Will that be okay with you?"

"Yes. Fine with me."

Both shook hands and Rahul left the principal's room.

That evening, Bhattacharya, Meenakshi and seven other teachers walked into the principal's room along with Politician Dikshit.

The principal was taken aback and exclaimed, "Sir, you? Here?"

"Why are you so surprised? Isn't this my school too? Can't I come to meet you and other colleagues as I wish?" then Dikshit added sarcastically, "or do I need someone's permission?"

"No, sir, this is your school, you don't need anyone's permission. Good you came, we have a special meeting. You can also participate in it."

At that moment, Rahul walked into the principal's room. He greeted everyone in the room politely.

"Take your seat, Rahul," said the principal. "Gentlemen, we had a meeting yesterday wherein Rahul took up the challenge of teaching the worst-performing students and prepare them to do their very best in final exams that are only nine months away. Bhattacharya will take students of his choice and both teams will compete. This is not a competition between teams, it is a competition between two theories or two methods which in my view are on two opposite extremes. On one end, we have Bhattacharya, who has around twenty years of experience in teaching. He must have taught around 8,000-9,000 students. No one can doubt Bhattacharya's experience and capabilities, thanks to such immense experience and knowledge.

"On the other hand, we have Rahul, an absolutely brilliant person and teacher, who has unprecedented experience and amazing success in the world of business, science and technology. He was the CEO of one of the world's top technology firms. It is our privilege that we have the opportunity to work with a man of his calibre. In his previous job, he had invented V-Office, a unique system of working for corporate companies, which could help us save billions of dollars, enormous amount of our time, make our planet green and a better place to live in. Personally, I'm amazed with this invention and strongly believe that we all will successfully adopt his suggested ways and lead a very peaceful life.

"Like his personality, he has a different ideology about teaching. He seems to have some radical thoughts and ideas, which, if implemented, can revolutionize the teaching-learning process all over the world. He is talking about the fundamentals of the human brain and mind, talking about learning and sharing knowledge. He has tremendous faith in people and their capabilities, and considers every child to be equal in terms of learning capabilities and hence puts the onus of a child's success in the hands of his elders, on his parents and teachers. He feels that our education system has failed as it has not been able to develop geniuses. All over the world, lakhs of students are passing examinations and graduating from schools, but the world is generating less than 1 per cent of subject experts and geniuses. Many years have passed since we have had an Einstein, an Arya Bhatt or a Da Vinci. What our current form of education has created are mediocre people. There is tremendous scope for improvement in the way we teach and train our young generation.

"So, gentlemen, here we have two different, totally contradictory theories. Rahul feels that it is not the child's fault if he does badly in his studies, whereas Bhattacharya feels that after the teacher has taught the topic to the student, it is only the child who is responsible for his performance in studies. Our school, Saraswati Vidhya Mandir, has always sponsored and promoted new ideas, which can help students and the teaching fraternity. I'm delighted to be a part of this debate and honoured to be appointed as judge of this competition between the two groups. This competition will be guided by the following rules and regulations, and any member from any group if found violating it, will be disqualified from this competition. In such a situation, the other group will automatically be declared winner. Here goes... both groups will select thirty students each; you will get the hall and one playground to train your group of students; school will be run as usual and the routine will not be disturbed; you will be free to select one more teacher from the available staff; and along with this teacher, you will be responsible for teaching all the subjects to the students. That's it, gentlemen. May the best team win!"

★   ★   ★

Next morning, as Madhuri walked into the school premises, she saw Bhattacharya, Meenakshi and a group of teachers from the other camp together. She wondered at the unfolding of events in the past few days: Rahul taking up the challenge, his vision, and his endearing personality.

As she was thinking about Rahul, a smile appeared on her face. She started looking around for him, but he was not to be seen anywhere.

'Where could he be?' Madhuri thought desperately. 'He is a gem of a guy, smart, intelligent, very helpful and innocent; he doesn't understand the dirty politics played by people like Dikshit and Bhattacharya, who are jealous of his intelligence and success. There is no comparison between Rahul and this bunch of people. They are out to prove him a failure by outsmarting him through such a challenge. What a nonsensical challenge is this! Why must Rahul accept such a challenge?'

But then, she herself came up with the answers. 'Well, that again proves his innocence and straightforwardness, but what about the challenge? How will he handle it? What if he fails? Will he leave the school?' Madhuri felt sad at the thought of Rahul losing the challenge and being forced to leave the school.

By this time, she had reached the right corner of the school compound where Bhattacharya, Meenakshi and around seven or eight teachers were standing and talking. As she came close to where they were standing, Bhattacharya came forward and greeted her.

"Good morning, Madhuri!"

"Good morning, sir."

"Have you come to check our preparations? Then let me tell you, we are going to defeat the opposite party. I have been teaching students for twenty years and can't go wrong."

She remained silent.

"Come with me."

Bhattacharya took her to a group of students who were sitting on the staircase, looking bored and hassled.

"I've selected the best of students, who have performed well in the exams in the last three years. Most of them have secured the first, second or third rank in the last exam. Now I will show Rahul what good teaching means," Bhattacharya concluded grimly.

Unable to bear the nonsense, she moved away from that place.

'Where is Rahul?' Madhuri pondered yet again.

*   *   *

Rahul swung himself out of the swimming pool. As he walked towards the changing room, his toned body looked perfect. His gait was straight and relaxed, as if he was involved only with himself, and not needlessly bothered by the surroundings. After changing into his clothes, Rahul walked towards one of the chairs that were arranged in the shade by the poolside, sat down, and waved at a waiter.

As the waiter came up to him, he said, "One fresh lime, please."

"No, make it two!" said someone from behind.

Surprised, Rahul looked around and was pleased to see Sunil Parekh. Sunil was Rahul's long-time colleague and a good friend in Gold Star, and now he was with the Washington office of the company.

"Hey, buddy!" exclaimed Rahul with joy.

He got up and hugged Sunil impulsively. Then he apologized, "Sorry, *yaar*, I've spoiled the crease of your shirt!"

"No problem, Rahul. Anything for you."

"When did you come from Washington?" asked Rahul as Sunil and he sat down.

"I came last night, called you up, but there was no reply. Then, this morning, I went to your house, heard that you are in the club, so I came here looking for you."

"Great! It's nice seeing you, especially after such a long time."

"So what are you up to nowadays, Rahul?" asked Sunil.

The waiter quietly came and placed their drinks on the table. Taking a glass each, they sipped as they chatted.

"I'm teaching in a school," Rahul informed.

Sunil was flabbergasted, "What?? You are teaching in a school?" he asked, incredulously, his expression was a mix of shock and deep amusement. Laughing, he said, "I can't believe that one of India's most successful technocrats and business leaders is teaching in a school! How ridiculous and atrocious, how can you do that, Rahul?"

Rahul leaned forward in his seat aggressively and raised his voice, demanding, "Why do you feel it is atrocious? Because it doesn't pay handsomely? Why is it that in our society and even in the minds of educated and elite people like you, teachers do not have the place they deserve the most? Teachers are the foundation of our society and country, as they are responsible for training and nurturing delicate minds... our children. If you can't appreciate them, it's okay but, please, for God's sake don't make such a face! It's hurting."

Sunil realized his mistake.

"Sorry, Rahul, my intention was not to hurt you or degrade the teaching community. I too have a high regard for teachers in my heart. I agree they are the foundation of our society. I'm really sorry. But I still can't believe that you have taken to teaching, leaving a world-class company and an enviable career."

"That's true. Anybody would be surprised with my decision and the turn of events, it's not your fault, Sunil," replied Rahul, somewhat appeased.

The two friends continued to sit by the poolside, chatting about some common friends, and who was doing what.

"Let's have some grub, *yaar*, I'm dying of hunger," Sunil said suddenly, one hand on his stomach.

They had finished their drinks by then, and Rahul looked at him, amused, "You haven't changed at all! Still hungry all day. Sometimes I wonder whether you have a devil in your stomach."

They strolled towards the club restaurant that overlooked the pool. As they sat down at a table, a steward approached them for their order.

Rahul asked Sunil, "What will you have?"

"Anything that you order."

"Is Italian food fine?"

"Sure."

Rahul flipped through the menu, and placed their order, "One pasta with white gravy and two servings of garlic bread, please."

"Anything to drink, sir?" asked the steward.

"Two glasses of beer. What all do you have?" piped Sunil.

"No, only one, I'll take a Fresh Lime Soda," and then clarified to Sunil when the steward had gone, "I have to go to school after this and, by the way, I've given up alcohol some time back."

"Why? But you enjoy beer immensely! Why have you changed so much, Rahul? First, you gave up your plum position at Gold Star at a time when they were ready to make you the global CEO. And then you take up a job which probably doesn't pay even one-tenth of the salary you used to get. What on earth happened, Rahul?" asked Sunil anxiously.

"It's my love for my son, Sachin. And, an attempt to earn his love and confidence. Not to lose him permanently," Rahul's voice became heavy with emotion, and, as he said the last bit, his eyes moist.

In the meantime, the waiter served their food and drinks. Over their meal, Rahul told him of his fractured marriage with Sheetal, and then the more recent events, detailing every instance, starting with Sachin's suicide attempt and his hospitalization, Sachin's confession why he attempted suicide, and his promise to Sachin that he will always be beside him, in every situation, helping him face every challenge in life.

As Rahul recounted those days to Sunil, the latter grew engrossed in the story, and his face wore a grave look.

After narrating the whole, personal story, Rahul concluded, "I have lived my life, now I want to live for him. Make him a bright student and a confident person in life."

With moist eyes, and feeling sad for all that his friend had gone through, Sunil said soberly, gently chiding Rahul, "Friend, so much happened to you and you never even informed me. You considered me an outsider?"

They both sat silently for some time, deep in their thoughts.

Then, noticing the time, Rahul got up from his chair and asked Sunil, "Are you free?"

"Nothing much to do, actually I'm on vacation for a month," Sunil leaned back in his chair, and said in a grave tone, "Rahul, my family and I are tired of staying away from India, so I'm seriously considering shifting back to India. I have had a discussion with my boss and he has okayed my transfer to our Indian office, which was once headed by you."

Rahul listened to him and said, "That's not a bad idea. Gold Star is doing great in India. Particularly after the introduction of V-Office, it has become the global centre for new developments. You will have a lot of scope here," then thinking, he added, "how old is your son? I think same age as Sachin's?"

Sunil nodded and said, "Once I shift, I would like to put him in a good school. May be you can help, now that you are a big teacher."

The last bit he said jokingly, and both of them started laughing.

"Sure, why not. Sachin would also like the company of your son. What's his name?" asked Rahul.

"Amol."

While they were talking, the waiter brought the bill. Rahul signed the bill and left a ₹500 note in the folder, as tip for the waiter.

As they started walking out of the restaurant, Rahul asked Sunil, "Then why don't you join me, I'm going to school. Today is the most interesting day of my life. I have taken up a challenge."

"What challenge?"

"I'll tell you on the way. Let's move from here."

They walked towards the main entrance of the club, going past the lobby and reception.

As they headed to the patio, Rahul walked to the parking lot for bikes; Sunil was taken aback. Rahul pulled out his bike and asked Sunil to sit as pillion.

Sunil couldn't resist asking, "Where is your Lamborghini, how come you are driving a bike? If I correctly recall, you didn't like bikes as much, then how come you are driving a bike now?"

"Life teaches you everything, my friend. It is the love for your loved ones that makes you handle the biggest trials in life. The bike is a small change. Come on," Rahul smiled as he patted the pillion seat of his bike.

Sunil sat on the bike, and they drove to the school. As they reached the school premises, they saw a flurry of activities going on. Bhattacharya, Meenakshi and their gang were happy having selected the best of the students.

Seeing Rahul, Bhattacharya strode towards him and said easily, "Rahulbaba, I thought you wouldn't return, that you were afraid."

"Afraid? Of what?" Rahul asked in a slightly annoyed tone.

"Of the challenge!" said Bhattacharya with a wicked smile. "We have made all the preparations, I have selected my batch students, and we have also decided who will do what. Have you carried out all such preparations?"

"No, I don't need to prepare. Why don't you do me a favour, Dada?"

"Tell me, Rahulbaba. I am at your service."

As they were talking, Madhuri came and stood alongside, listening to their conversation.

She said, "Bhattacharyaji, please don't worry, I will prepare for Rahul Sir. I will select students, teaching partners, etc."

Bhattacharya looked disappointed. Rahul could see it from his face, so he looked at Madhuri and said, "Madhuri, if you don't mind, let Bhattacharya prepare for my group. I want to use his experience."

"But Rahul–" she objected but Rahul stopped her by waving a hand at her.

"I trust him. Whatever he does for us, will help us do better in this challenge. More importantly, it will be better for the students whom he will select. Am I right, Mr Bhattacharya?"

Bhattacharya, virtually bouncing with enthusiasm and joy, at Rahul's reply, quickly answered, glancing at Madhuri, "Yes, yes, why not? After all, we are colleagues and friends," then turning to Rahul, he said, "Rahulbaba, I will complete the activity by tomorrow morning, you can come and take charge."

"That's fine," said Rahul and walked towards the principal's office along with Sunil.

At Principal Sir's office, he knocked on the door and asked for the former's permission to enter.

"May I come in, sir?"

"Rahul, don't be formal, when I'm alone you don't need my permission to do anything, because I'm sure whatever you will do will be good for both the school and students."

"Sir, you are putting blind faith in me!"

"Yes, and I will continue to do so."

Rahul introduced Sunil to the principal and said, "Sunil, meet Mr Roshan Daruwala, Principal of this school and my friend and guide," and then turning towards the principal, he said, "This is Sunil, my friend and ex-colleague at Gold Star Electronics. Sunil was in the US and now he wants to return to India. He wants to take admission for his son in our school."

The principal smiled at Sunil and shook hands with him.

The Cooked-up Selection

NEXT MORNING, AS Rahul was parking his bike, Madhuri came running to him. She looked terribly upset.

As she came near Rahul, she started arguing with him, almost immediately, "Why did you give Bhattacharya the responsibility of selecting students for your team? I protested but you didn't listen! Now see what Bhattacharya has done!"

Rahul, not able to understand what she was trying to say, gave her a puzzled look and asked, "Can you please explain what has happened? Where have I gone wrong? What has Bhattacharya done that cannot be corrected?"

As the answer to his questions, Madhuri simply grabbed Rahul's hand and led him towards the Art Hall.

The Art Hall in Saraswati Vidhya Mandir was a smaller hall compared to the auditorium. Like other halls, it too had a stage, had a seating capacity for about sixty people, and a big area in-between. As Rahul and Madhuri entered the hall, Rahul could see

Bhattacharya and Meenakshi talking, laughing and clapping each other on the back. Thirty students sat on the chairs, looking nervous and tensed – quite the opposite of Bhattacharya and Meenakshi, who were looking extremely happy. Some of the students were talking to each other in whispers. The hall was resounding with the laughter of these two men. Their backs were turned towards the door, so they didn't see Rahul and Madhuri entering the hall and approaching them.

They continued with their ongoing dialogue, "Now the fun begins. Let us now see how Rahulbaba wins this challenge!"

Rahul walked up to them, and without any hint of stress, smilingly addressed the maths teacher, who didn't look one jot uncomfortable that Rahul had overheard his jeering remark.

"Bhattacharyaji, this is not a challenge where one team has to win. It is a competition between two ideologies. Whatever we are going to do in the next nine months will be for the benefit of the student community and not for your or my gain. We are going to experiment and as it could happen with any experiment, we may not see the desired results. You may win, or I might win. It is also possible that we will witness a wholly new outcome which none of us had ever thought of! Whatever may be the outcome, I suggest we maintain honesty and fairness in our approach. At the end of this exercise, I am sure I will find a good friend in you."

Bhattacharya did not look impressed. His face clearly indicated that he did not agree with what Rahul had just said.

He said, "Rahulbaba, I appreciate what you are saying. I will also ensure that we have a fair fight. But this is a competition, so one of us has to win," then looking at Madhuri, he added, "yesterday you asked me to select students for your batch so I have completed that task for you. See, how much I'm cooperating – but here you are doubting me unnecessarily."

Then, as though he had just remembered something urgent, he turned to Rahul and said, "I have to rush for my next class, Rahulbaba – we will meet the principal in the evening."

Bhattacharya, along with Meenakshi, rushed out of the door.

In the evening, the principal convened a meeting in the auditorium. When Rahul reached the auditorium, it was full; all committee members were sitting in the front row, followed by teachers depending on their seniority; students of higher classes were seated behind teachers, while the last row was occupied by office bearers and supporting staff. Practically every individual linked to the school was present in the auditorium. Rahul noticed that Madhuri was not there. 'Perhaps she is unhappy with the whole arrangement made by Bhattacharya,' he told himself.

The principal requested both Rahul and Bhattacharya to come on stage. Also seated on the stage were the chairman of the school Mr Batliwala, ex-Principal Mrs Kaminidevi, and leading educationist Mrs Sushmita Mukherjee. Rahul and Bhattacharya both sat down on chairs that had been set aside for them, next to Principal Daruwala. Rahul looked at the audience; all eyes were on the stage, with anxiety and curiosity.

Principal Daruwala got up from his chair and walked towards the microphone.

"Good evening, Chairman Shri Batliwala, Respected Mrs Kaminidevi and Sushmitaji, staff, friends and students. It is my privilege to welcome you all to today's function, which in my opinion, is going to begin a different chapter in the history of our school and of the education system. If we have the blessings of Devi Saraswati, this day will be remembered as a golden day in the history of education, not only of our school, state or country but of the education system all over the world!

"As you all know, our school has always taken the lead in doing things differently. We were the first in introducing co-education; we were also the first in introducing English as the medium of instruction; we sponsored and encouraged sports for boys and girls and we were again the first to waive fees for girl students. We have always encouraged innovation in all our activities, primarily in finding new ways of imparting education and knowledge to tender-aged students. We have a very successful track record – for the past ten years, we have been maintaining 100 per cent success results; our students occupy the first five positions in the SSC board exams; our students also have been doing well in sports.

"I am happy to announce one more such initiative which has originated from a small debate between two teachers: Rahul Saxena and Mr Bhattacharya. Rahul Saxena who has joined our school six months back, has had a very successful career as CEO of the world-famous Gold Star Electronics where he invented V-Office. On the other side, we have Mr Bhattacharya who has a rich experience of around almost 25 years in teaching. He must have taught about 8,000-9,000 students. The recent discussion on teaching methods started over a small debate on who should be responsible for the academic performance of a student: the student himself or his teachers and parents.

"Bhattacharyaji and almost all teachers, barring one or two, are of the view that while the teacher can impart good knowledge and education to students, the ultimate success of each student's capability to learn depends entirely on the student himself. Their argument is that it is practically impossible for the teacher to get involved with each of the 150–200 students and ensure they have learnt. This theory is further supported by the argument that because grasping the essence of what has been taught by the teacher is the responsibility of the student, you have a wide difference in the performance of students studying in the same class and in the same environment. This theory is also validated by what we have been experiencing in our day-to-day life; despite being exposed to the same learning imparted by the same set of teachers in the same class, some students stand first, whereas some fail.

"On the other hand, we have Rahul Saxena bringing in fresh thinking, suggesting that learning is primarily in the hands of elders, teachers and parents. His argument is based on the belief that all human beings have the same level of intelligence and capabilities; the difference, however, is due to training and environment. His argument, which even I agree with, is that as toddlers all children in school demonstrate the same level of learning. But as they grow up and go to higher classes, differences in individual performance widen, which is mainly due to the conditioning of their minds and understanding of the subject. Rahul's theory gives us a completely new perspective, which is worth looking into, worth experimenting.

"I'm now inviting Bhattacharya and Rahul Saxena to take charge of their own teams and introduce their students to all of us."

Bhattacharya looked at Rahul and asked, "Can I first introduce my batch of students?"

"Sure," replied Rahul, waving his hand in agreement.

As this was going on, Rahul noticed Madhuri entering the hall. She was perspiring and breathing heavily. 'Perhaps she's rushed in,' Rahul thought. She sat down on a chair in the front row.

Rahul smiled at her, but her response wasn't very enthusiastic. 'May be she is tensed,' Rahul told himself.

Bhattacharya started announcing the names of the students he had selected for his team. Now it was Madhuri's turn to react, it seemed; she looked more and more anxious as he announced the names. All of Bhattacharya's batch students, chosen from Class IX, were the best in that class. He had chosen ten students each from sections A, B and C, and they were all toppers in their respective sections, and stood between the first and the tenth positions.

As Bhattacharya came to the end, loud applause filled the hall. Then it was Rahul's turn.

Standing in front of the microphone, Rahul began, "Before I announce the names of my students, I wish to thank Mr Bhattacharya who has done me a favour by selecting all the students in my team. Frankly speaking, I do not believe in forming such batches or groups, but since it is a necessity in this competition, I'm accepting it."

He took out a chit from his trouser pocket and started reading out the names of the students in his team.

"Shankar Sukhdev, he is a dedicated student. Besides devoting day time in school, Shankar works in a restaurant at night to support his family."

As Rahul spoke about Shankar, the screen in the auditorium displayed his marks in the last two class tests.

Subject	Class test 1	Class test 2
Maths	5/50	7/50
Science	15/50	12/50
English	8/50	7/50

"Gautam...

Subject	Class test 1	Class test 2
Maths	9/50	15/50
Science	13/50	17/50
English	18/50	17/50

"Sapna Pradhan...

Subject	Class test 1	Class test 2
Maths	13/50	17/50
Science	18/50	15/50
English	9/50	7/50

"Ameya Mahajan...

Subject	Class test 1	Class test 2
Maths	8/50	9/50
Science	19/50	13/50
English	8/50	7/50

"Murali Ramakrishnan...

Subject	Class test 1	Class test 2
Maths	5/50	7/50
Science	15/50	12/50
English	8/50	7/50

"Sachin Saxena...

Subject	Class test 1	Class test 2
Maths	13/50	17/50
Science	18/50	15/50
English	9/50	7/50

"Samir, star bowler in the school cricket team...

Subject	Class test 1	Class test 2
Maths	13/50	17/50
Science	18/50	15/50
English	9/50	7/50

"... he is a budding player but poor in studies," Rahul had by now progressed to Samir. "He failed in mathematics and science in the last couple of exams. Samir loves to play sports; he's good in cricket, swimming and athletics... Samir has won many medals for the school in inter-school competitions.

"There are 22 more students in my team, who don't seem to be doing too well in their academic performance. They have been selected by Mr Bhattacharya as well."

As Rahul finished his speech, there was a huge uproar amongst the students present in the auditorium, who started shouting against Bhattacharya.

"Bhatta Hai Hai!"

"Be fair to Rahul Sir!"

"This is injustice, how can you do such a thing to a newcomer and a gentleman like Rahul Sir!?"

Various opinions disapproving Bhattacharya's move started emerging from the audience. As if on impulse, Madhuri got up from her seat and raised her hand, looking at Principal Sir and the chairman, Mr Batliwala.

Mr Batliwala looked at her and then taking the mic, sternly ordered the audience to be quiet.

"Please be silent! Here we have Ms Madhuri wanting to say something. Can we listen to her, please?"

As the protests and grumblings started fading from among the audience, the chairman looked at Madhuri and said, "Can you please come up on the stage and tell us what you want to say?"

Madhuri started walking towards the stage. She seemed to be walking at an unusually fast pace as if she was in a hurry or was too anxious! She walked up to the microphone and spoke in her clear, firm voice.

"Sir, thank you for giving me an opportunity to express my views. I just want to say that this whole process of batch selection is a big hogwash. It is one-sided and totally unfair to Rahul Sir, who is new to our school and the whole profession of teaching. With no offence meant, I just want to add that Mr Bhattacharya has taken undue advantage of the trust Rahul Sir had placed on him. Just look at the academic performance of the students in Mr Bhattacharya's group – they are all bright students with a proven track record of coming among the first ten rank-holders in different sections. Now compare them with the academic performance of the students in the batch allotted by the same Mr Bhattacharya to Rahul Sir. I do not wish to discourage or demean the students in Rahul Sir's batch but when we are talking of a competition or a challenge, there must be a level playing field."

Just as she finished expressing her brief but powerful opinion, there was an outcry in the audience, particularly from students. Once again, students started shouting against Bhattacharya, who was by now quite embarrassed. He got up from his seat and without even bothering about the presence of senior committee members, started defending himself.

"Look, I was requested by Rahulbaba, so I obliged. Why else would I have bothered? You people decide and allot another batch team to Rahul. I simply cooperated with him. And you guys are accusing me of unfair practice.

"I applied the same logic that Rahulbaba has been preaching: that all students have equal capabilities. The difference in their academic performance is the environment created by teachers and parents. If all students have the same capability, how does it matter who is part of Rahulbaba's batch – students with a good track record or those with a not-so-good record?" he looked at Rahul and concluded in a mocking tone, "what do you say, Mr Saxena?"

Rahul felt the force of the tone, but as usual, he chose not to react. He just smiled.

Seeing Rahul smiling, Madhuri became more restless and she urged Rahul, her anger obvious now, "Why don't you say something, Mr Rahul? This is not to be taken lightly. It is a question of not only your reputation but the future of students as well!"

As she finished, Rahul got up from his seat and walked towards the microphone. He first looked at Madhuri and then addressed the auditorium.

"Many thanks for your concern for the success of my philosophy of teaching and the future of our students. It is really heartening and encouraging to see people taking this philosophy so seriously even before it has proven itself!

"In the *Bhagwad Gita*, when Arjuna asked Lord Krishna, how could he be expected to kill his own brothers and elders, Krishna told Arjuna that he was just an executor of the fate of his brothers and elders, which had already been decided! This fate was the consequence of their deeds, so Arjuna could neither be associated nor held responsible for the outcome. It was because of their deeds that they would be dying – defeated – on the battlefield of Dharma – righteousness and natural justice – at the hands of a suitable person, in this case, Arjuna. So when their fate had already been decided, it was immaterial whether Arjuna agreed to be the executioner or not. If Arjuna had declined to fight, someone else would have fought and acted for Dharma, and his brothers and elders would have met with the same pre-decided end. Now, the real question was about Arjuna's *faith*. Did he have real faith in the leadership and teachings of Krishna? Did he really think that Dharma was beyond feelings and relationships? Did he really commit his capabilities for the betterment of the *yug*, looking beyond benefits for self and family relationships? Then he should not have so many doubts in practising Lord Krishna's teachings.

"In this case too, it is a question of *faith*. Do I have faith in myself? Do I have faith in the capabilities of these young students? Do I have faith in my philosophy that excellence in any field is the outcome of interest and dedication, and it is never dependent on the choices or decisions of a selected few? If the answer to all these questions is *yes*, then I do not need to worry about the fairness of Mr Bhattacharya's selection of my team members. My philosophy should apply equally to all, irrespective of their last academic performances. It may not be appropriate to blame Mr Bhattacharya for his selection as I had requested him to do me this favour. He did the selection, he thought to be suitable and appropriate. Does the success of my approach and philosophy depend on Mr Bhattacharya's selection? In my view, the answer is *no*, so I am neither reacting nor complaining."

As he finished, Principal Roshan Daruwala stood up and started clapping. He said, "Mr Saxena, I fully agree with your thoughts. Philosophy and belief in oneself are never slaves of circumstances and inputs. I am impressed by your ideas and really look forward to witnessing the outcome of this competition."

This resulted in a loud applause in the auditorium. Madhuri's eyes were full of tears. She left the hall in a hurry.

As usual, Rahul had a mild, confident smile on his face. Everyone was happy and enthusiastic, except a few like Bhattacharya, Politician Dikshit, and Meenakshi… were they depressed? Perhaps one thought was playing in their minds: 'was the outcome of the battle decided?' Only time would tell.

Sharpening of the Axe

"WHY AREN'T YOU happy to be in my batch? I can ask Bhattacharya Sir to include you in his batch, if that's what you want," Rahul said to Gautam, the physically challenged student in Rahul's batch.

Although a bit short for his age and slightly on the heavier side, Gautam, with his fair complexion, brown eyes and sharp features, was a handsome boy. But, while God had been kind to Gautam by blessing him with good looks, he had deprived Gautam of his right leg, which was paralysed by polio.

Gautam's eyes became moist and he said, "No, sir, please don't say that. It is my pleasure to be in your team. As a matter of fact, I consider myself lucky that I'm born at the time when leaders and teachers like you are present."

"Then what's the issue, Gautam?" Rahul was puzzled by the boy's behaviour.

"Sir, all of us who are in your group would like to meet you for some time. What time is convenient for you?"

Rahul cooled down. He realized that his exasperation with Gautam was unwarranted.

"Gautam, my son, you don't have to take my time, I'm always available for you, but since all you kids want to meet me, let's meet in the teacher's room at around 5pm. Is that fine?" Rahul suggested.

"Yes, sir, that's fine with us. Your availability is important; we, on our part, will manage our time," and thanking him, Gautam went off to his class.

Wondering what it was all about, Rahul slowly headed to his class. At 4.45pm, as he got free from his work, Rahul went to the staffroom.

He was surprised to find Madhuri waiting outside the room. "Good evening, Madhuri!" he greeted her.

"Good evening," she replied with a smile.

"Are you waiting for me?"

"Yes."

"Come on in. The children will be joining in some time."

Rahul opened the door of the room and walked in. Madhuri followed. It was a clean and tidy room, measuring around 600sqft, with a large wooden table placed at the centre. One large-sized executive chair stood behind the table, with around twenty chairs on the other side; there were some smaller desks at one side of the room. Rahul sat on the executive chair and asked Madhuri to sit down. She sat down on one of the chairs.

"Well, you can tell me now," Rahul asked her, once they had both settled down. "As a friend and colleague, you are always welcome but it seems that today you have a special reason to meet me. What's the matter?"

"You must leave this school," Madhuri said bluntly.

"What? Why?" Rahul was taken aback, he couldn't believe his ears. "Are you asking me to leave this school? You mean that I resign from this post and go away?"

"Yes," confirmed Madhuri calmly.

"But why?"

"Because you are being made a scapegoat by some people. They want you to lose this challenge and spoil your name and reputation. You see, you come from a different background. Things are different here, totally different," Madhuri began earnestly. "Nothing has changed in the last ten years of my being with this school. It's the same set of teachers, same managing committee and, every year, the same type of tests and exams. Only the students keep changing, but they too are in the same monotonous state – attend classes, grab what they can; the students in the higher classes find the teaching here inadequate and so they also take up tuition classes. They appear for exams, most are successful, some fail. Those who pass the exams, move on in life; those who have failed, re-appear and pass or give up studies. This has been the routine in… I can't tell for how many years… but certainly during my tenure with this school."

She paused to catch her breath, sipped water from one of the glasses kept on a side table in the room, and continued.

"Then you joined us, you brought fresh thoughts and ideas, but I don't think people here deserve it. You must leave this place, it's not meant for people like you. It is full of people like Bhattacharya who will just pull you down every time you try something new, to secure their position," she stopped abruptly.

Rahul noticed she was breathing heavily, her eyes had become moist by now.

As Rahul opened his mouth to say something, there was a knock on the door.

"Yes? Who is there?" shouted Rahul.

"Sir, it's me… Gautam."

"Come in," said Rahul, and opened the door to let the boy enter the room.

Gautam entered timidly. Sachin, Samir, Shankar, Sapna Pradhan, Ameya Mahajan, Murali Ramakrishnan, and a few others accompanied him. Rahul smiled at them and asked them to sit down.

They greeted both Rahul and Madhuri and sat down, facing Rahul.

"Yes, tell me, what do you want?" Rahul asked Gautam, who in turn looked at Sapna.

She started, "Sir, we all want to tell you something."

"Okay, go ahead."

"Sir, we students, all of us, who have been selected as part of your team, feel that injustice has been done to you."

"Why do you think so?" asked Rahul, surprised. He looked at Madhuri, who conveyed through her eyes her agreement with what Sapna had just said.

"Sir, look at the academic performance of most of us in our group – and when compared with that of students in the opposite party – we all feel that it's not fair to you."

Dumbfounded, Rahul couldn't help repeating, "Opposite party?"

"Yes, I mean students in Bhattacharya Sir's batch."

"Oh, I see," then glancing first at Sapna and then at Madhuri, he said, "even your favourite Madhuri Ma'am feels that injustice has been done to me. Can someone please explain to me how it has been done?"

Sapna replied quickly as if the question was expected and her answer was ready. Her swift response showed that she had been mulling over this particular topic for a long time.

"Sir, most of the students in our batch have a pathetic academic record in the last few exams. If we look at our marks in the last three exams, you will know what I'm talking about!" Then, hesitantly, she added, "Don't mind my telling you, sir. We all feel that by leaving your batch selection to Bhattacharya Sir, you have made a mistake. He has taken all the bright students in his group and allotted the below-average students in your batch, who under no circumstances will get better marks than that of Bhattacharya Sir's students. So in this way, despite your good intentions and willingness to do good for us students, you will lose the challenge and one of the best attempted intentions and efforts for the well-being of weak students will be wasted."

Sapna's eyes had become moist as she was saying this. Rahul saw that Shankar, Gautam and Ameya had also become emotional, tears flowing down their cheeks.

The next moment, they were all standing, hands folded, and beseeched Rahul, "Sir, please, cancel this challenge or at least ask for better students so that your name and reputation does not get tarnished and the trouble-makers do not succeed."

Madhuri added, "Exactly, Rahul, this is what I told you some time back."

Rahul could sense their nervousness. With the intention of cheering them up, he looked at them and said, "Friends! I'm proud to have all of you as part of my team. I'm honoured to have all of you in my batch! You all are unique in your own way, but you don't seem to be aware of your strength, your humility. I firmly believe you are all intelligent, talented and quite capable, perhaps more than the students who might be scoring better marks.

"But the problem with all of you is that, over a period of time, you have successfully learnt to *doubt* yourselves, which is blocking your success. If I have your cooperation and support, I'm sure you will all perform to the best of your capabilities. Are you all ready to take on the next challenge of your life that will not only transform your performance at studies within school but even after?"

Rahul noticed that the expressions of the students were changing, even as he was speaking, from total hopelessness to one of hope – and then to one glowing with hope!

Rahul resumed, "You are all part of a big revolution which is going to change the way students gain knowledge. If you call Mr Bhattacharya's group as 'students', I would like to recognize all of you as 'scientists' – as those who do not merely restrict themselves to knowledge given in books or what is relevant for the exams, but who are in constant search of more knowledge and understand the process of evolution of that knowledge. In a way, they do not merely perform well in one or two exams or tests but, over a period, contribute towards the development of world's knowledge in every field – be it science, technology or even history! Are you all ready to be part of this exciting journey?"

The students were eager and excited by now. They shouted in unison, "Yes!"

Their response was so loud, that it virtually resounded in the school, as if there was a loud clap of thunder. Even those who were not present in the room such as Bhattacharya, Meenakshi, students of Bhattacharya's batch, the principal and many others felt the energy that radiated from that room that evening.

Rahul said briskly, "Good! In that case, I want each one of you to come prepared tomorrow with a one-pager note, with your name, an introduction on your family, your likes and dislikes, and the activities you enjoy the most. Moreover, I want to check your preparedness, so each one of you will prepare on one subject. Shankar will prepare in English – you will give a short description of your visit to a theatre or a movie that you've seen; Gautam, you will study a chapter in history; Sapna, you will do mathematics; and Ameya, geography. I will call all members of the school to participate in this preparedness test, so prepare well."

Saying this, Rahul nodded his appreciation, and left the room, followed by Madhuri and then the students, one after the other.

*　　*　　*

The next day, at 10am, Shankar stood on the stage, bursting with confidence.

"Okay, Shankar, please describe in English, the story of the movie you saw last."

"Okay, Rahul Sir. The name of film was *Pretatma* – story of a *bhoot* getting into body of heroine and *satawing* her."

"*Satawing?*" asked Rahul, unable to understand what the boy actually meant.

"*Satawing* means troubling," explained Madhuri with a smile.

Shankar continued, "Movie started with big *haveli* gates opening *apne aap kuchud… kuchud…*"

"*Apne aap?*" again interrupted Rahul, not able to get the story.

"Means without help," Shankar clarified, and then complained, "Sir, *aap bahut* disturb *karte ho.*"

"Okay, I won't interrupt. But you must narrate the story clearly, so that I can understand."

"I will try, sir. I know my English is difficult to understand for common men," added Shankar proudly, and proceeded, "sky *mein chamgadhad* flying round and round."

"*Chamgadhad?*" Rahul could not understand again.

124

Shankar looked at Madhuri and said, "Ma'am, a bird who sleeps in the day and remains awake in the night."

"Bat you mean," Madhuri pointed out.

"One man walks into the gates and moves *or haveli.*"

"Moves *or haveli?*"

"Moves towards the *haveli,*" Shankar explained, which resulted in a loud burst of laughter among the listeners in the auditorium. "He fights on door of *haveli.*"

"Fights with doors, how?"

"Sir, you are disturbing a lot, my whole penetration *ka bashpibhavan* happening."

"Penetration *ka bashpibhavan?*" everyone present chorused together.

Shankar raised his hands and pointed towards his eyes with first two fingers. Next, he raised his thumb and moved it, denoting a 'no'.

Madhuri said, "Do you mean to say, you are not able to concentrate?"

"Yes, see how easily you are able to understand," said Shankar, completely unaware of how pathetic his understanding was of the English language.

By this time, the whole group was in splits of laughter. Seeing so much laughter all around him, Shankar felt rather encouraged. Madhuri asked him to continue.

Shankar said, "He fights with the door. Door open *apne aap.* He moves into the *haveli* with lot of tension on his face. Why I came here, he told himself. As he moved into the big hall, it was quite dark, not able to see anything."

As expressions of fear started appearing on his face, Shankar proceeded with his narration, "He was carrying a torch, so he switched it on and what he was *dekhing?*"

Rahul had, by this time, decided not to respond and allow the story to flow.

"He *dekhoed* that, past tense *hai na* is *liye* 'ed' is put on '*dekho*'," he stopped to simplify, and then moved on, "he *dekhoed* a big painting of a beautiful lady in the right hand *khobcha*. Curious enough, he moved towards the painting. As he moved closer, he observed *khoon* coming out of her eyes. His *pasina chhut gaye*, he became *stabdh*, not able to move. Suddenly there was some noise from behind, he *ghooma* noise *ki* or to *dekhing ke* same *ladki* in painting was standing in front of him. His heart *dhadking* fast, *pasina chhooting*, he felt he will *behosh hoing. Tab tak ladki* moving *uski or*. He did not know what to do. *Achanak* his guts coming, he folded *mutthi* and told himself '*bhag Milkha bhag*' and started running door *ki or*."

There was fear in every students' eyes now.

"As he was *bhaging darwaje ki or, darwaja achanak* closed… *dhadam*… now what? Man thought. That girl was having big laugh, 'He-he-he, ha-ha-ha. *Main tujhe kha jaungi*. Ha-ha-ha.' She came near to man and *lambaving* her hand towards man's *gardan*. Man noticed she had big *nakhun* with blood on it. Hands touched his *gardan* so he started going *pichhe, pichhe*, she was moving more and more *aage* and suddenly he fell down in a *kuan*, his body hit the ground. As he opened his eyes sleeping on the ground, he saw same lady with wide big deadly eyes and telling him to get up. He shouted with big force, '*Bachao, bachao dayan* has come, *dayan* has come.'

"Suddenly there was big slap on his face, the pain of which opened his eyes, he saw his wife in a furious mood and complaining, 'Is this a way to describe own wife a *dayan* and that too in the morning?' His wife started crying only then man realized that was his dream!" and so Shankar's narration ended.

Rahul then asked Gautam to come on stage.

When Gautam stood on the stage, Madhuri asked him, "Gautam, tell me, Sikander *ko kisne mara*?"

Fearfully, Gautam replied, "Ma'am, I've not done that. Someone has misinformed you."

Madhuri said, smiling, "I'm not talking about Sikander in your class. I'm talking about Alexander the Great. Tell me, how did he die?"

"Oh, *aapne toh dara hi diya*," then pretending as if he was pondering on the question, Gautam started murmuring, "Who killed Alexander? Hmm…"

"Okay, let's move on. Why did Maharana Pratap fight the Mughals?"

"Must be for land?"

"Stop it!" shouted Rahul at the top of his voice, "Stop it!"

Taken aback, the whole batch fell silent. No one had thought he could react so strongly. Madhuri, too, looked surprised, even shocked. There was pin drop silence in the auditorium.

He continued, furious, "Is this what you have learnt so far in your studies? What poor learning skills!"

He moved towards Shankar and said harshly, "You are in Class IX and still can't describe a simple incident in English. So many mistakes in English! Your vocabulary, grammar, sentence formation – there are mistakes everywhere."

Grimly, he next pounced on Gautam. "And you, you're taking this class as a joke? Who killed Sikander? Of course you did not! That is an old joke! Are you here to crack jokes and make people laugh? Or are you here for a purpose? Enough is enough! I'm tired of this casual attitude towards this whole exercise. You may think studying and learning is a joke, but unfortunately it is not!

It is a question of your life and career. If you are not at all serious about it, then I'm not interested in taking it forward. I will surrender to Principal Sir and Bhattacharya, and concede defeat – of my principles and philosophies. I will tell them that it is not possible for me to take on this challenge as I have failed to ignite passion for knowledge among my batch of students."

Throwing his hands up in the air in desperation and anger, Rahul walked out of the auditorium. Everyone was stunned, and in that silence Madhuri could hear her own heartbeat!

'Is it the end of a big and promising dream?' she thought. Perhaps she was unable to read the situation.

The Saviour

THE NEXT DAY, as Rahul got out of bed, he decided to meet Principal Sir in the morning itself; he would admit his failure and withdraw from the challenge. He hadn't slept well the previous night. Although he had woken up early, he didn't feel like going for his usual round of morning walk, so he decided to get ready for school instead. He looked around for Sachin, who was not to be seen. He must have left for school.

"I'm sorry, Sachin, but under the current circumstances and the level of involvement of the students, I have no option but to give up," feeling bad for Sachin, Rahul muttered to himself, while taking out his bike from the garage.

As he entered the school, he saw Madhuri waiting for someone. He parked his bike near the school building.

Madhuri came up to him and greeted him, "Good morning. I was waiting for you."

"Good morning, Madhuri, I'm sorry for what I did yesterday, I couldn't control myself and just had to walk away. I don't think they are serious and, therefore, I've decided to tell Principal Sir that I'm accepting defeat."

Madhuri noticed his tired eyes, puffy with lack of sleep. His disappointment was obvious to her.

"They are all waiting since morning to meet you. Can you please come with me?"

"No… what is there to talk about?"

"That's not fair. Why don't you meet them once and then decide?" she urged.

Rahul appeared to be in two minds, but then he agreed hesitantly. Madhuri led Rahul towards a little ante room next to the staffroom, where they had all met the previous day, and opened the door. Rahul saw his students waiting for him.

As soon as they saw Rahul, they all wished him in one voice, nervously, "Good morning, sir!"

"Good morning!" replied Rahul, cold and distant.

He put down his backpack, and seated himself. Then he looked straight at the students, one by one, sternly. Abruptly, Shankar and Gautam came forward and folded their hands. Shankar spoke first.

"Sir, I'm sorry to disturb you. But yesterday… that wasn't intentional. My English is not good. I come from very poor background, where I have to work very hard to even survive. But I have deep hopes to turn around my and my mother's lives through education, because that's the only hope left. But due to my background and situation in the school, despite the intention I was not able to perform better and continued to do worse in every exams. Then when I first heard you on the day when you played cricket with all of us, I saw a saviour in you, there was a ray of hope in my heart. Then the competition got announced and I got selected in your batch, my hope strengthened further. I even told my mother about getting into your team and she was also extremely happy that now I will get an opportunity to fulfil her dream about my future."

As he explained his behaviour and his situation, Shankar's face grew apologetic. He looked at Rahul with eyes full of hope, and tears slowly filled his eyes.

He continued, "Sir, please, don't leave us alone, I promise to do whatever you will tell me to do. If you leave us now, my life will be ruined, I and my mother will die..." he choked, and started crying profusely.

By now, the other students had also become emotional and all of them were close to tears as well. Shankar's innocent appeal and helplessness touched Rahul, and he got up from his chair to cheer him up. As he came near Shankar, he raised his hand and patted his shoulder gently.

Shankar let out a piteous cry of pain.

"What's happened?" asked Rahul, alarmed, and took a step back, involuntarily.

"Nothing, sir."

"Why nothing? You must tell Rahul Sir the truth."

Madhuri, who had been a silent observer all through the exchange between Shankar and Rahul, now got up impatiently from her seat, as she spoke, irritated.

"What truth?" Rahul was still puzzled, and glanced first at Madhuri and then at Shankar.

"Nothing, ma'am. It's not important. Leave it."

Shankar was clearly frightened as if he had seen something horrifying. Rahul and the other students became quite anxious. 'What is he trying to hide?' Rahul wondered, gazing at Shankar, trying to figure out what was going on.

"What are you trying to hide? Tell us the truth. We will try to help you to the best of our abilities," Rahul urged the boy.

Madhuri moved closer to Shankar and asked him to remove his shirt; he did so with great reluctance. Rahul and the students were shocked to see wounds on his chest, and when he turned around, they were horrified to see that Shankar's back bore similar gashes. By now, the other students were openly crying. Madhuri, who obviously knew what Shankar had been going through, looked rather distressed and upset. Shaken into silence, Rahul too became emotional, his eyes turning moist.

After some time, when he had composed himself, he asked Shankar in a very hard voice, which was unusual to his soft and kind nature, "How did this happen? Who has beaten you? Who has done this to you?"

Shankar remained quiet.

"I'll tell you," Madhuri intervened. "Shankar was thrashed by the local *dada* of the slum where he stays, Rajiv Gandhi Nagar. It is in Vile Parle East, about 2km from the school. His father is an alcoholic, and doesn't have a job. His mother works as a domestic help and her income is not enough to meet the demands and expenses of his father, who needs alcohol every night. So, to meet his needs, Shankar works in the liquor bar of the local slum lord, Dagdu Dada, who in exchange of Shankar's services, provides his father with his daily quota of liquor. This arrangement suits both Shankar's father and Dagdu Dada, and this poor boy is trapped in-between them. If he resists, either his father or Dagdu – sometimes both – beat him up. And this is obviously affecting his studies. His mother had come to me for help, and I spoke to Principal Sir but we haven't been able to do much so far."

As Madhuri put Rahul in the picture, her voice was trembling with anger, her eyes full of tears, which started rolling down her soft, pink cheeks. In spite of himself and the situation at hand, Rahul just could not stop himself from looking at her face!

⋆   ⋆   ⋆

The next day, as always, the school bell rang at 5pm sharp. As the students rushed out of their classes, making a thunderous noise, Rahul went near Class IX B, where the students of his group were standing.

Looking at the children, he asked, "Who knows Shankar's house?"

After learning from Sapna that she knew Shankar's house, Rahul asked her to be ready at 8.30pm, he would pick her from her house. After picking up Sapna, Rahul drove down to Rajiv Gandhi Nagar. It was around 9pm when Rahul and Sapna walked into Rajiv Gandhi Nagar.

Rahul was smartly dressed in a brown half-sleeved round-neck T-shirt, and a pair of trousers of the same colour. His clothes complimented his lean and muscular frame.

As they neared Shankar's house, they heard a loud noise.

Turning to Sapna, Rahul cautioned her, "I think there is some disturbance in this area. Please stay here, I'll just see what's going on there, okay? Don't move till I come back."

"Okay, sir."

Rahul hastened towards the direction of the noise. What he saw stunned him. Madhuri was arguing with a big, stout man. With her right hand, she was holding Shankar's hand, while she held the right hand of the man with her left hand. She looked ferocious; Shankar looked frightened whereas the stout man looked baffled, as if he didn't know how to react. About seven to eight men stood nearby, holding various kind of weapons such as hockey sticks, pipes, sticks, etc. The heavy-set man looked at them and ordered them to stop.

Madhuri looked at the man, who was clearly a goon and the gang leader, and told him firmly, "Shankar is not your slave, if you have given liquor to his father, ask *him* to work for you. Why are you penalizing Shankar every night? Don't you know it is illegal to make a child work in your shop?"

The goon started laughing loudly, supported by his gang of thugs, who joined their boss in the laughter.

"Huh, I don't care if it's legal or not. He works at my shop in exchange for the liquor I give his father every night... his own father's made this arrangement! Now, you don't interfere or else..."

"What will you do if I interfere?" Madhuri demanded. "He is my student. You think he has no one to protect him, and so you keep harassing him and his mother! I won't tolerate your *dadagiri* anymore.... He will not work for you anymore, do whatever you want to do," she fumed.

Quite dazed at what was happening, Rahul realized that this stout man was Dagdu.

The thug responded, snarling, "Huh, who are you to tell me all this? Don't you know who I am? People can't escape my terror. And Shankar's dad is indebted to me, so this boy has no option but to work at my place. Nobody can stop me," and he suddenly pushed Madhuri, who was unprepared for this, and she stumbled, letting go of Shankar's hand. As she tried to regain her balance, he again shoved her hard, a look of contempt on his face. Madhuri hit her head on a nearby wall, and fell on the ground with a thud.

Seeing Madhuri fall down, Dagdu laughed loudly and looking at an accomplice, said, "Look at her, she wanted to beat me. Now she is licking the dust on the ground," then added, "get an ambulance for her."

Alarmed and angry, Rahul ran towards her, lifted her in his arms, and placed her gently on a bench that stood next to a ramshackle tea stall. Next, he gestured Shankar to stay by her side. Suddenly, a woman came out from the crowd, running towards Rahul.

"Madam is hurt!" she screamed at Rahul. "This guy is really notorious. Please call the police. Call the police!" she pressed, looking at the crowd. Seeing no response, she ran away from the crowd.

Looking at Dagdu, Rahul grimly said, "Now, *you* will call the ambulance."

Dagdu looked at him dismissively, and said, "And pray, who are you? Why have you come here to interfere in my work and die?"

Rahul replied, "I'm Shankar's teacher. We will not allow you your autocratic ways to dominate and spoil the life of this child."

Listening to Rahul, Dagdu laughed and taunted, "Who will stop me? You, a teacher?"

He smiled ominously. Rahul could see his yellow teeth had a brownish tinge. Dagdu was both ugly and dangerous.

Enraged, Rahul swiftly moved towards Dagdu and kicked him on his right thigh. Dagdu stumbled at the impact, regained his balance, and massaged his thigh with his right hand. He stood up, ready for a fight.

"So, you want to fight. For this kid?"

"Yes, Shankar is just a kid for you, but for me he is my student, my son. I will not allow you to play with his life."

Dagdu charged at Rahul and aimed a punch on his face. The latter was prepared, so he ducked and swiftly stepped aside to the left, which made Dagdu lose his balance, and the goon took two steps forward, facing Rahul. At this, Rahul raised his right leg and kicked him on his face. This proved to be a double whammy for Dagdu: first, losing his balance and, second, getting a kick on the face. Blood started oozing out of Dagdu's nose.

"You're misbehaving with a lady, no respect for women, right? Now, this kick will remind you that women are to be respected, every time!"

After being thrashed in front of the slum dwellers, whom he used to lord over, Dagdu became violent, his face distorted with rage. He snatched a hockey stick from one of his accomplices, swung it in midair to bring it crashing down on Rahul's skull. But Rahul had anticipated such a move, and before Dagdu's stick could come down, he kicked Dagdu's stomach hard.

Rahul's kick acted like a speed-breaker, which used Dagdu's force against his own power combined by his heavy bodyweight and the speed with which he was moving towards Rahul. He reeled, the sudden impact throwing him off-balance, and since he had been rushing towards Rahul at high speed, Dagdu hit the ground with a big thud. He tried to stand up, but was unable to do so due to the intense pain that ran through his body.

While still attempting to get up, he glared at his gang of thugs, who had been watching this fight that had hardly lasted some minutes, and roared at them, "Hey guys, what are you all looking at? Hit this b*****d! Teach him a lesson that he'll never forget in his life!"

As his gang walked towards Rahul menacingly, suddenly one of the thugs, perhaps in his thirties, came forward from the group of people, unexpectedly halted in front of Rahul and said, "Stop! Don't hit the teacher. My daughter studies in his school and we can't hit the teacher. I was against Dagdu hitting the lady teacher, but he would not listen. Don't you see? He is not an ordinary teacher who will be afraid of our sticks and kicks...? He is modern-day Dronacharya who knows how to wield weapons in times of crises. I've been telling Dagdu to spare this boy, but he didn't listen. So, he has met with his fate! Let's not disrespect Teacher Sir's position. Dagdu has also hurt the Teacher Ma'am who is lying on the bench, let's get her to a hospital."

That man was Abdul Rahim.

As he was saying this, a police jeep came up to the gathering, and screeched to a stop. Its siren, that had grown loud as it approached the crowd through the winding lanes of the slum, was turned off. The sudden silence was eerie. A police inspector, along with seven to eight constables walked towards them. It was Inspector Javed Khan, and he recognized Rahul, and approached him, grinning.

"Oh well, it's you again! Why do I always meet you at such odd occasions only? The last time I met you in the hospital, one boy had attempted suicide so there was tension there, and now when I'm meeting you here, there is tension again," then laughingly, "are you a tension man?"

"No, inspector. It seems that helping suffering children has become my destiny. That time it was my own son, who had attempted suicide, which had created the tension," and then pointing a finger towards Dagdu lying on the ground, Rahul added, "and this time, it is because of this guy that my student is suffering, so I had to come here to protect him."

Inspector Khan looked at Dagdu and recognizing him, he said, "Oh you! Dagdu Dada... troubling everyone in the area. Now that I've got you, let me take good care of you."

He ordered the constables to pick him up and put him in the van.

Thanking Inspector Khan, Rahul went near Madhuri who was still lying unconscious on the bench. Rahul asked for a glass of water. A lady from a nearby house got a glass of water and gave it to Rahul. He sprinkled some water on her face. After a few moments, she stirred and moaned in pain.

Rahul tried to wake her up from her semi-conscious state, and called out her name loudly, "Madhuri, Madhuri… get up!"

Hearing Rahul's voice, she slowly opened her eyes. Rahul noticed that she had difficulty in opening her eyes.

Gradually, Madhuri regained full consciousness. She still seemed to be in acute pain, which was visible on her face and in her glazed, drooped eyes.

Recognizing Rahul, she asked, "Rahul Sir, you here?"

Rahul put a finger on her lips and said, "Don't speak. You are safe now. Everything is alright."

She got up from the bench. Holding her by the shoulder, Rahul led Madhuri towards the doors of an ambulance, which had been called by one of the local women.

As they made their way to the ambulance, a stout lady emerged from the group of people still hanging around, and greeted Rahul with folded hands.

"Namaste! My name is Shantabai. I am Shankar's mother. You and Teacher Ma'am took so much trouble for Shankar – Dagdu hit her, too! I am thankful to both of you. You are a real saviour; you have saved Shankar's life and his future," her eyes were brimming with tears.

Rahul asked Shantabai and two more people from the locality to accompany Madhuri to the hospital, while he would join them on his bike after picking up Sapna from the place where he had asked her to wait.

The ambulance drove Madhuri to the hospital. Its loud siren disturbed the short-lived silence after the fight. Rahul walked to the place where he had parked his bike. People were still standing around in silence, with a look of awe in their eyes. After all, someone had single-handedly broken the goon's ego and bones – Dagdu who had created so much fear in their minds, was now in police custody. As Rahul walked down the path, people stepped back and gave him way, on the road and perhaps in their hearts too!

After picking up Sapna and dropping her home, Rahul drove down to the hospital.

Four people in four different locations – Rahul, Madhuri, Shankar and Sapna – were thinking about the same incident but with different perspectives. Rahul and Madhuri had seen each other in a different and aggressive form, while Shankar and Sapna had seen their teachers in a new light, who were not only caring people but who could also risk their own lives and fight devils to save and nurture the lives of their students.

As news of this incident spread among the batch students, their level of confidence grew manifold; confidence in themselves and faith in their teachers!

The Dream Merchant

IT WAS A Sunday. Lying on the sofa in his home, Rahul was thinking about the events of the past few days. Bhattacharya's selection of students, forming batches, and his partial and self-centred behaviour; Madhuri's and others' outburst on hearing the background of his group of students; Shankar's hilarious narration of the movie he had seen; his decision to quit; apology offered by the students and their plea to him to continue; Madhuri's new *avatar* at Rajiv Gandhi Nagar; and finally saving Shankar from Dagdu's tentacles.

The more he recalled Shankar's face and that of his hapless mother, the more certain and confident Rahul became about the success of the competition. And the failure of Bhattacharya's views. Rahul's desire to win was not for any personal reasons, but to help millions of aspiring students like Shankar, Gautam and his batch students, who wanted to be successful in studies but were unable to even pass the exams because of boundaries created around them!

These students are victims of ignorance and negligence of the system, be it in their families, in school and even outside!

'Corrective measures have to be taken,' Rahul thought, 'to bring them out of the current situation so that they enjoy their studies, gain and share knowledge, apply it, and have a bright and promising future.'

Abruptly, as if some thought had occurred to him, Rahul got up from the sofa, picked up his mobile and dialled a number.

"Hello, Madhuri! This is Rahul. Can we meet all our batch students tomorrow at 8.30am?"

"Sure, I'll call them, and give them your message."

"Thanks," said Rahul and disconnected the line.

★　　★　　★

It was Monday morning, 8.30am. Rahul's batch students had gathered near the auditorium. Madhuri, who too had turned up by then, was surprised to see all the students present before time. 'This is the first time I'm seeing all of them on time,' she smiled to herself. There was a small garden outside the auditorium, with a couple of garden benches; she strolled over to one, and sat down on it. After a while, she found herself studying the faces of the students: some were anxious, some excited, a few nervous. Each one had these emotions in different degrees, though. Like Gautam... he looked quite excited as if he would get to know something new, something different; Shankar, on the other hand, looked nervous. Sapna looked curious as if she wanted to know what was there in store for her. Ameya Mahajan looked indifferent as if he was not interested in all these developments; he sat in a corner, playing with a leaf in his hand. Murali, too, looked excited; unable to hide his feelings, he walked up and down the corridor. He even asked Madhuri twice or thrice when Rahul

141

Sir would come, which indicated his eagerness. Like Murali, some others looked upbeat.

After about 15 minutes, Rahul arrived with Sachin as pillion passenger. Madhuri kept looking at Rahul, appreciatively, as his bike approached the auditorium. As soon as the bike came to a halt, Sachin got down from the bike and rushed to his favourite teacher, Madhuri. Rahul, in the meanwhile, drove to the parking bay in the school. Sachin looked very cheerful. 'Perhaps because his daddy is with him,' she thought.

Having parked his bike, Rahul walked towards her.

"Good morning, Madhuri, good morning, kids."

"Good morning, sir!" the students chorused loudly, in one booming voice.

Momentarily taken aback at the enthusiastic, deafening response, he smiled at them and told them to come with him to the auditorium.

As the students seated themselves in the auditorium, Rahul set up the projector.

When he was done with it, he faced the students and asked them, "Why do you all want to study?"

Murali promptly raised his hand.

Rahul smiled at him, "Yes, tell me, Murali, why do you want to study?"

"Sir, I want to study so that I can support myself. If I study well, I will be able to choose the type of work I wish to do or I can do, and lead a dignified and independent life."

As Murali said this, his sad voice touched Rahul who walked up to him and patted him on his back.

Then Shankar's hand went up.

"Yes, Shankar?"

142

"I want to help my mother and give her a comfortable and dignified life. Mother tells me if I study well, I can become a big officer and earn lots of money like you, sir, and buy a big house like a *laatsaab*!"

Everybody in the auditorium started laughing at the way Shankar said it.

Rahul raised his hand, indicating that he wanted silence in the auditorium. He looked at the students and said, "You all want to study and come up in life. But that you can do even without education. There are so many people who are not educated, yet they still made a fortune in business, or lead a successful life. More than earning money and leading a good life, education has a lot to do in your life: it shapes your personality. It gives you an opportunity to make an immense impact on the lives of millions of people now and in the future. Let's look at the video which I have prepared for you all."

Saying this, he switched on the projector. Madhuri got up and switched off the lights in the auditorium. As the audio-video presentation started, silence fell in the auditorium, all eyes focused on the unexpected audiovisual treat.

"Dear students, the journey of learning started since the evolution of mankind. As you all know, we have evolved from apes. Since humankind is the most intelligent of all animals, humans always worked hard to make their life better and their work easier. It first started with hunting. Humans had neither the strength of the elephant, nor the speed of the cheetah, nor eyes as sharp as the eagle, nor the agility of the monkey or the squirrel. Neither did humans have the jaws and teeth of the tiger, the skin of the rhino, nor the venom of the snake. In that way, there was nothing that humans had that could give them an edge over other animals. Yet, humans survived; they live the longest, and they have also established their supremacy because of their intelligence. This intelligence inspired humans to do things differently, which could add to their power, capabilities, comfort and safety. To increase their power, they built weapons, right from the catapult in earlier days; then progressed to bows and arrows, to guns and in the modern age to very powerful bombs and missiles. To improve their capability, they built machines, which helped them do far more difficult work within a shorter timeframe. The invention of the wheel, which led to the development of various utilities like carts in earlier days, eventually led to cars and a range of vehicles in modern times. This made them capable of travelling thousands of miles in significantly less time. Machines also enabled humans in almost every field such as agriculture; you have tractors for ploughing and sowing the field, thrashers to separate grains, mills for making flours and modern-day mixers and grinders in your kitchen to help you prepare your food at an amazing speed.

"Humans also built machines for comfort; the architecture of the bygone era shows ways of keeping homes cool through unique ventilation designs, to modern-day's fans and air conditioners and heaters which help you beat summers or winters and live in comfortable surroundings. Our forefathers built cars and airplanes to travel long distances with ease, and also made them more comfortable through air-conditioning.

"In all this, humans also ensured increased safety of their fellow beings. Today, of all animals, humans live the safest of lives. They live in well-protected colonies and buildings, use electricity to keep their homes well illuminated, use electronic gadgets to ensure that unauthorized people do not enter premises, have mobiles phones to communicate instantly with anyone he/she wants. In other words, humans have ensured supremacy of their lives through constant improvement of their knowledge, which is updated through the process of continuous learning and development. This process of continuous learning and development is followed in modern times through education, which is imparted to everyone, especially children and the youth, in schools and colleges, institutions and universities. Tell me, would you not like to contribute to this exciting process of building knowledge for your fellow human beings? To be part of the ongoing revolution of life? Or, do you want to live a passive life like a plant in your house or a pet dog at your home!

"We have many great scientists, philosophers, saints and sages, architects and mathematicians, who have made great contributions in the fields of science and technology, arts and literature, architecture, agriculture, roads and transportation. It is because of them that we are living a comfortable life today. It is now your turn. Let us look at some of the technological marvels that we have experienced in the last five decades, which have in them the power to change our lives forever.

"Cellular Telephony: A form of an advanced wireless communication. It redefined the way people communicate with each other and conduct day-to-day business and other activities. With mobile phones, you are able to connect to an individual, irrespective of his/her geographical location, make an instant communication and get the job done. This results in incredible saving in time, costs and enables us to handle emergencies. With cellular mobile technology, you can also have machine-to-machine communication, which can be used in irrigation, meteorology; vehicle-movement tracking and a large range of activities that can help us save millions of lives, and ensure optimal utilization of earth's scarce resources.

"Internet: Connecting millions of people on earth, simultaneously at the same time and communicate, transact business, carry out an activity, entertain or educate without any limitations of time or distance. This is the power of the Internet. With the Internet, you can connect remote villages, towns and human settlements that are located in otherwise inaccessible areas. The Internet can enable people in distant parts of the earth to stay connected and educate themselves with latest developments.

"Space Research: After reaching the moon, mankind has carried out a vast range of research activities in space. Experiments have been carried out on gravity, the black hole, and artificial man-made satellites are launched in the earth's orbit, which helps us check and predict changes in weather, arrival of the monsoon, tides and other environmental changes. This capability can help us prepare for emergencies like cyclones, floods and save millions of lives. In the last five years, developed countries like the US, Russia, China and India have also carried out missions to Mars to check weather conditions, possibility of life, etc.

"Medicine and Healthcare: Human life is most precious. We have carried out amazing research in fields of healthcare treatment of dreaded diseases such as cancer, hypertension, diabetes, depression, and other mental disorders. Incredible developments have happened in enabling disabled people who suffer from polio, dysfunctional spinal cords – even amputees. Earlier, these people were bedridden. Now, with the synergy of medicine and engineering, equipment have been developed which not only help them overcome their deficiencies but also empower them to lead a very active, successful and dignified life."

At this point, Rahul stopped the projector and switched on the lights of the auditorium. He was surprised to see the incredible amount of excitement and enthusiasm in the eyes of all the students. They were all wide eyed and had smiles on their faces.

Suddenly, Ameya, who normally kept quiet, got up from his seat and said, "Sir, I want to study very hard and become a good doctor so that I can spend my life in research work, which can help crippled people lead a comfortable and independent life."

Sapna, Murali, Gautam, Shankar, Sachin and other students of the batch broke in, telling Rahul eagerly that they all wanted to study hard and reach a level where they could make significant contribution in peoples' lives.

Rahul raised his hand once again, and the group grew quiet.

"It is good to know that you all want to study hard and earn specialization degrees and name, but it is not easy, you will all have to make big sacrifices as well. Learn well, study hard, drastically cut down on watching TV and playing games. Will you be able to do that? Will it be possible for you? Can you all–"

Before he could finish, there was a thunderous response from the children gathered there in the auditorium.

"Yes sir, we can, we will!"

"Do you all promise me to put in your best effort? I will be very strict and very tough with you all, and will make each of you work very hard – are you sure that you will not give up?" Rahul asked them again.

"Yes, sir, we will not get tired, we will not quit, we will enjoy."

Madhuri couldn't believe her eyes as she took in the gusto and readiness of the students to do their part of work to achieve success in their studies and life. The fervour and determination in the auditorium was catching – she found herself wishing that she too was a student again, and learn under Rahul.

Tit for Tat

IT WAS AROUND eight in the morning. Murali and Gautam were walking towards their class, and they had to go up a flight of stairs to reach their class. Usually, the staircase was a favourite place for students: they would sit and do their work here, and it served as a preferred meeting place for students as well. As they approached the stairs, Murali asked Gautam to hand over his bag to ease the load on his shoulder. Gautam initially refused, but finally relented at Murali's insistence.

As Gautam slowly climbed the stairs, it was apparent that he was finding it difficult due to his disability. When they had reached the stair landing, he suddenly tripped, and fell. Laughter rang out from one side of the staircase.

Murali looked around and saw Shiv Dikshit laughing loudly along with his friends. Controlling his temper, Murali turned back to Gautam, who was feebly struggling to get up, but unable to do so due to an injury in his left leg and his own physical disability. Murali reached out to him, and helped him get up.

Shiv Dikshit, son of Politician Pratap Dikshit, was well known in the school for his notoriety and bullying. Generally, Murali would not have given much importance to his prank, but he felt

Shiv had crossed the limit that day. He had no right to trip Gautam, play a prank on him, a physically challenged child!

After helping Gautam to stand up, he led him towards a corner, sat him down on the steps, and turned towards Shiv and his gang, who were still sniggering.

"This is too much, Shiv! You have no shame, you are troubling someone like Gautam and that too in such a cruel way. If you do such a thing again, I'll hit you and break all your teeth."

In response, Shiv and his gang laughed even loudly.

"You don't believe me, I see. I don't want any trouble today because I have to take care of Gautam, but I will not spare you the next time. I'm warning you, don't you dare do any such thing ever again."

Shiv and his gang were still chuckling, as if Murali's warning had no impact on them.

Sneering, Shiv said, "Why are you feeling bad, if Gautam has fallen down? You guys are losers, and will be losing against our team. Haven't you seen the kind of students in our team, all bright scorers?"

He was referring Bhattacharya's team as 'our' team.

Murali interrupted him, "Excepting you, who has been in the same class for the last two years. It appears you will retire from this school only."

As Murali said this, Shiv's friends, as well as those present within earshot, started giggling. This irked Shiv, who got up from the step on which he was sitting, came up to Murali, and caught him by the collar of his shirt. He raised his left hand to hit Murali, when suddenly there was a loud thud and he felt acute pain shooting up his left leg. Loosening his grip on Murali's collar, Shiv turned around to see Gautam standing up, leaning on one crutch; he had raised the other crutch, ready to hit him a second time.

Furious, Shiv rushed at Gautam, leaving Murali, but even before he knew it, he came crashing down on the hard ground of the staircase landing. Initially stunned, Shiv felt unbearable pain in his right hand, as if it was broken. The other students rushed forward to help Shiv, lifted him and made him sit on a stair.

Meantime, on learning about the incident, Anjali – who was the principal's secretary – sent four office assistants to control the students, and send help for Shiv. By the time the office assistants arrived, the fight was over and Shiv was sitting on a step with a swollen right hand, surrounded by students. His face had turned pale, because of the acute pain.

After learning of Shiv's injury, two assistants went off to the school clinic and returned with a stretcher. They gently placed him on it, and took him to the clinic. Lying on the stretcher, Shiv lifted his head and tried to look back. He could see Murali and Gautam shaking hands over their so-called victory. Murali turned, looked at Shiv and raised his hand just as a victorious soldier would raise his sword after winning a battle. In excruciating pain, Shiv rested his head on the stretcher and closed his eyes. Gautam and Murali headed towards their class as if nothing had happened!

As news of the fight spread through the school, the situation at the clinic, turned chaotic, since students had started to gather there, their curiosity getting the better of them. Teachers and other staff members, who had heard about the incident, rushed to the clinic. Principal Daruwala also arrived and started enquiring about what had happened. Students rattled out different versions, Shiv's gang of friends giving an entirely different story than that of the others. While the principal was trying to understand the conditions under which the confrontation took place, Politician Pratap Dikshit came rushing.

It was obvious that he was livid, as his son had got hurt, but far greater than his son's injury was his own ego that was smarting.

He started shouting, "What sort of school is this? Innocent students are being hurt by *goondas* within school premises!" then, looking at Principal Daruwala, he accused him, "and you remain silent! You must call the *goondas* immediately and rusticate them from school. Such *goondas* are responsible for spoiling the environment of the school..."

He would have continued, but the principal pacified him, made him sit down on a chair and asked an office boy to get him a glass of water.

The principal next looked at the crowd and sternly asked them to disperse, "Right, all of you here, please go back to your classes. Shiv is fine now."

The principal called Murali and Gautam in his office, later in the evening that day. Also present were Shiv, his right hand in a cast; his dad Pratap Dikshit, Bhattacharya, Meenakshi, Madhuri and Rahul. Outside the room, Murali's and Gautam's parents and guardians were anxiously waiting to hear the outcome. Murali's parents looked quite pensive. His father, Ramakrishnan, looked tense and grim, while his mother was weeping.

He tried to console her, "Don't worry. Nothing will happen to our son. He will never fight with anyone without reason," but it was quite ineffective as he himself was not convinced.

Inside the principal's office, Dikshit looked at the two boys angrily, "So these are the *goondas* who beat up my poor son."

Rahul immediately objected, "Don't call them *goondas*, they are students of the school. We can't label them as accused until facts are known to us," then, looking at the principal, Rahul continued gravely, "sir, I have heard incidents of bullying by Shiv. About eight to nine other students support him, and together they have formed a gang to tease and harass students, particularly girls and weak students. However, you may please carry out an enquiry."

At this, Politician Dikshit barked, "Look at this man! Today my son has been hurt and Rahul Sir is accusing him only. This is grave injustice!"

Rahul looked at him straight in the eyes, and said severely, "It's not an accusation but a fact. You may ask any student in the school and they will all tell you the same. This has been going on for quite some time, and even today when these two boys were going up the staircase, it was Shiv who started the trouble. He tripped Gautam, who is physically challenged; and he fell down on the floor. And, then, instead of helping him get up, Shiv and his friends laughed at them. Obviously, Gautam could not do much, but his friend Murali who was with him, got angry and he got into a scuffle with Shiv. Even then, instead of apologizing to these two boys, Shiv tried to silence them by fighting with them. He was injured in this fight. It's a simple story of Shiv's bullying other students that turned awry for him."

Then looking at Shiv sternly, Rahul said, "Is this true, Shiv, or would you like to add anything?"

Shiv did not look at Rahul, but looked down and remained silent.

Glancing at Pratap Dikshit, Rahul said, "I can understand your feelings towards your son. But he is on the wrong path, so you need to correct him. Just look at his academic performance; he doesn't study, and instead creates mischief in school. Everyone remains quiet because those students who speak out against Shiv are taken to task by him and his gang. As for the teachers, they are hesitant to talk to you directly, as they are afraid of you."

Pratap Dikshit stood up, looking fierce, and threatened them, "This is incorrect, I will see you all," then he said to Shiv in Marathi, "Let's go, son, we will find a way to take care of these people later."

Shiv got up from his chair and looking at Rahul, Principal Daruwala and others present in the room, started walking towards the door.

"Wait a minute, Shiv."

A heavy and powerful voice uttered these words. Stunned at the commanding tone, everybody in the room was taken by surprise when they turned towards the speaker. It was Principal Daruwala. Generally calm and soft-spoken, the principal looked very different at that moment; he was livid. Infuriated, he ticked off the politician.

"Mr Dikshit, listen to me carefully. This school, which we also regard as a temple of Devi Saraswati, must maintain its purity and serenity. If I get a complaint of Shiv's bullying from any student or teacher ever again, I will be the first to take disciplinary action. Not only Shiv, but anyone in the school premises or even outside, is found to be bullying or ragging other students, physically or mentally, irrespective of a boy or a girl, will be dealt with severely and suitably punished."

Both Dikshit and Shiv were dumbfounded as they had never expected such a fierce response from the principal, who in the politician's opinion was like a rubber stamp, flexible and used as per convenience, with no guts. 'Now even rats have started roaring; it is because of you Rahul, you will get to know what I am capable of soon,' he said to himself, and stomped out of the room, his son in tow.

Don't Pity, Empower Yourself

THE DAY AFTER the Shiv episode, around 8.30am, Rahul was walking towards his class when someone greeted him.

"Good morning, sir!"

It was a familiar voice; he stopped. Gautam was walking towards him. He saw that the boy was looking rather downcast that morning. Gautam came closer to Rahul and once again said, "Good morning, sir!"

"A very good morning to you, Gautam! How are you?"

"Not very fine, sir... I'm very sorry for what happened yesterday. But I swear on God, we didn't begin the fight. It was Shiv who tripped me," replied Gautam, looking miserable.

"Cheer up, Gautam, that is a thing of the past. You don't need to bother about what happened. Not your fault."

Gautam looked at his crutches, asked earnestly, "Then whose fault is it, sir? Why am I like this?"

Rahul realized that he was terribly upset, his eyes mirroring his distress.

"What's the problem, my friend?"

Gautam continued morosely, "Why am I like this? Weak, orphaned and disabled. Totally dependent, helpless and hapless."

By this time, Madhuri arrived with the other students, but they remained silent as they saw Gautam's cheerless face.

Rahul could sense Gautam's anguish, thanks to the previous day's incident. Shiv's bullying had frightened him. Gautam's daily struggle of overcoming his feeling of being weak and helpless had given way to his fear and frustration, which had risen to the surface. Rahul realized this and hence allowed him to speak.

Almost in tears now, Gautam continued, "I lost both my parents in an accident in my childhood. I was three then; I don't even remember what my parents looked like! My uncle and aunt raised me, they are both good people, but couldn't give the kind of attention and love that my own parents would have given. They forgot to give me the polio dose, and so I got polio; now I'm stuck with these crutches for life. Why only me, sir? Why is it that every time there is any suffering, it is Gautam? Even yesterday, when I was going my way, Shiv stuck out his leg, and I fell down. Why don't people realize that my falling down, which makes them laugh, causes pain in my body. And more than my body, it breaks me from inside. Even when I'm walking on the road, many people imitate me. It hurts me when they behave so.

"Why don't they realize that I am also a human being? I too have my self-esteem, which nosedives because of their actions and attitude. Sir, physical injury heals over time, but this injury of mind and heart... it leaves permanent scars. My confidence and self-respect gets shattered with every such experience."

Gautam, who had emptied his heart of his anguish and grief, and had spoken for quite some time without a pause in-between, began to breathe heavily. Rahul asked someone to get a glass of water for him. Murali went out of the classroom and returned with a glass of water. Rahul sat Gautam on a chair and asked the other students, who were visibly upset at Gautam's predicament, to come close.

After some time, when Gautam had sufficiently recovered and was composed, Rahul asked him, "Gautam, do you know which is the weakest of all animals? Or name the animal that does not have *any special* capabilities?"

Gautam thought for some time, but when Rahul saw that he was unable to find the answer, Rahul looked at the others and repeated the question. Uncertain, they looked at each other, and kept quiet. Rahul looked at Madhuri and repeated the question.

Madhuri hesitantly said, "Is it mankind?"

"Absolutely correct!" turning to the students, Rahul told them emphatically, "just think of any capability and you will realize there are many, much more capable animals on the earth. We have a weak body, we don't stand a chance against an elephant or a hippo; we have weak eyesight, and can't beat an eagle or an owl; with our weak legs we can't run faster than a cheetah, and we don't have the kind of muscle power that a horse has. Yet, we are the most advanced than all animals in the kingdom. Do you know why?"

The children were listening to him with deep interest. Even Gautam had forgotten to cry and was staring open-mouthed at Rahul, taking in everything that he was saying.

"Because we have an intelligent brain and a powerful mind, which has always inspired mankind to do incredible things. We have enormous courage and belief in ourselves that has led humankind to incredible progress that no other animal has been able to achieve. Let's talk about belief. For example, we all know man cannot fly since we don't have wings, but if I ask you, can we fly, what will be your answer?" while asking this question, he looked keenly at the students.

By now, they were deeply engrossed in what he had been saying, so they replied unanimously, "Yes. We can fly. We have airplanes, helicopters, and now rockets... so not only can we fly but we can also travel to outer space."

"Excellent," remarked Rahul and then looking at Gautam said, "see, you and your friends have started becoming smarter."

Gautam smiled weakly, and nodded his head.

"It's a matter of common knowledge that humans cannot run fast. Certainly we cannot run faster than the cheetah, but can you move faster than the cheetah?" was Rahul's next questions to the students, who again replied enthusiastically.

"Yes, we can move faster than the cheetah, in a car or bike or even truck."

As the students responded promptly, Gautam too started enjoying the ongoing discussion.

Rahul pointed out, "The same is true for other capabilities like eyesight, physical strength, etc."

He paused for some time and continued, "So in a way, despite being physically weak, today we are no more weak or helpless. Do you know how it became possible? It became possible due to the vision, belief, courage and confidence of a few, who were also humans but they had different mindsets.

"The Wright brothers dreamt of flying when the whole world believed that humans couldn't fly. But, they didn't allow their belief to get diluted by what others thought or believed. They dreamt of flying so they went ahead and built their own plane. Their first flight lasted for only 10 seconds in the air. Did the

Wright brothers stop and give up? No, they pursued and achieved what they had dreamt of: flying.

"Similarly, before Thomas Alva Edison invented the light bulb, people used candles, lanterns and whatnot. Did he accept darkness? No, he dreamt and believed that there could be light at all times, and he invented the light bulb. Was he influenced by what others were thinking or doing? No. He had faith in his own dream and belief."

Rahul paused, noting the attentive faces in front of him, and proceeded, "In that way, we have hundreds of examples of people who did not get influenced by what others said or did; instead, they carved their own path and set an example for the world to follow."

Rahul turned to Gautam, "You are living in your own world, which you believe is crippled. Your problem is not disability of the body, but you have developed a disabled mind, which is not setting you free – to dream, to try and achieve. Every time, you see some challenge, you immediately hide behind your disability and self-pity. You don't even give it a try! What you are today is not due to your disability but it is because of your lack of dreaming and trying."

Then he thumped his hand on the table and protested, "Why can't you dream of becoming the most successful doctor or a scientist and develop a solution for millions of crippled people around the world? How can you play cricket, when you have never ever attempted to get free from your crutches and walk? How long will you hide behind your disabilities and cripple your imagination and creativity? Just get up and start working for what you want to be and what you should be! None of us has taken birth to pity ourselves. If we can't believe in our own capabilities, how can you expect others to believe in us? And that would be the death of a spirit in you."

Having said what he had to say, Rahul sat down on a nearby chair.

After hearing Rahul's inspiring speech, the children kept quiet for a while, thinking. All the students were moved, while Gautam was smiling.

He went to Rahul and said, "Sir, you've made me realize that I've been giving too much of importance to my physical disability. That made me develop a disabled mindset too, and so I stopped dreaming, stopped trying. Every time I came across any opportunity to improve myself, I saw an even greater obstacle in my way in the form of my disability and doubted if I would be able to do it. Mostly, 'doubt' won and I never pursued the opportunity. But, starting today, I'm not going to limit my thoughts and capabilities anymore. Sir, I've decided I want to become a doctor. Will you please help me prepare for this big challenge?"

The students stood up and cheered for a long time. Rahul looked at them, everyone was extremely happy at Gautam's transformation and his decision to stop wallowing in self-pity. He looked at Madhuri; she seemed to be in deep thought. Knowing her nature by now, Rahul guessed that she was, in all probability, thinking about Gautam's dream, which looked almost impossible to achieve. Was it realistic for Gautam to dream big?

Who is Responsible for Performance?

IT WAS SUNDAY morning; Rahul got up at 5.30am. He changed into his tracksuit, walked to the park near his house, started jogging, completed 5km, and then followed it up with his regular exercises – stretching, pull-ups, dips and kicking – on the green area designated for these. It was his daily practice, to get up at 5.30 in the morning, jog, and then exercise for around 45 minutes.

He came home, showered, got ready for school and went to the dining room for his breakfast. Sachin had already finished his breakfast. The day before, he had messaged all the parents of his batch students to meet him at school at 10am sharp. His message was stern and uncompromising. When he reached school, parents had already occupied their seats and were waiting for him. Madhuri informed him that the parents of all the batch students had come except Shankar's and Ameya's.

He nodded his thanks, went to the dais, and addressed the gathering over the mic.

"Good morning, friends. I'm grateful to all of you for attending today's session in full strength and encouraging me and my team members. My name is Rahul Saxena and I'm one of the teachers in this school. You might be aware that this school, where your ward is studying, has taken up many innovative programmes that constantly seek to improve the standards and methods of education/imparting knowledge to the students. I'm in charge of one such initiative and your ward has been selected to be part of this initiative."

He stopped now, and looked around. All the parents were keenly listening to him and there was pin drop silence in the auditorium.

He continued, "Around two weeks ago, I had an argument with an experienced teacher in this school. The argument was about who should be held responsible for the success or failure of a student in school. The student himself or his teachers and parents? This particular teacher strongly believes it is solely the student who is responsible. The job of the teacher is to impart knowledge and thereafter it is up to the student how much he picks up. He further supported his argument with the current scenario in schools that how is it that when all students in the same class have been given the same information, some students get higher marks, while some students in the class also fail. So the student who stands first in his class has best understood the knowledge imparted by the teacher, and the ones who have scored less or those who have failed are the ones who have not picked up as desired."

Saying this, he paused for a moment and then asked, "By the way, those who agree with this teacher, please raise your hand."

Almost everyone in the auditorium raised his or her hand.

161

"Oh, almost all of you also believe the same."

Gathering his thoughts, Rahul resumed, "Now let me put across to you another theory, which draws on a famous quote by a great leader and emperor – all people are born with the same intelligence, there is nothing like dumb or genius – and I fully agree with him. As per information available from the physiological view point, till the age of these students, everyone's brain is the same, with the same memory, same capability. So as per medical data, all students have similar capabilities to learn and perform."

He stopped briefly, trying to gauge people's reactions. Most of them looked baffled, as if unable to decide whether Rahul's statement was true or not.

One parent got up from his seat and said, "But sir, if it has to deal with studies and learning, I agree with the first theory. You have so many students in class, some stand within the first five or ten, most pass scoring average marks, and some fail. If people have the same memory, the same capability... then all of them must produce similar results."

"Can anyone of you tell me, what do we mould or develop in the hundreds of students who attend school every day?"

"Future," replied someone from a corner of the auditorium.

"Shape their minds!" was another voice coming from another direction.

Rahul looked at a parent who had raised his hand and asked him, "Would you like to guess, sir?"

"We shape their behaviour, we teach them discipline."

"Attitude!" said another parent.

"All of you are partly correct in your guesses, but if I have to describe it in one word, I would say we shape their interest in attaining the knowledge. We intend to do just that; but does it actually happen? No, it doesn't happen," he paused, looked around and continued, "that's the reason why children – who score 90–95 per cent in KG – get poor marks in their studies as they grow older.

"We had carried out a survey of students in KG. The survey results showed that most students in KG score good marks in tests, mostly in mid-nineties out of 100 in most subjects. They have displayed excellent memory recall.

"But have you ever wondered why the same tiny tot who is very sharp in KG, and scores amazingly good marks at the primary level starts losing out in marks as he/she grows up? And, by the time they are in the seventh or eighth standard, we have perhaps four categories of students: Outstanding, those who come in the first five positions in the class; Clever, those who come up to the tenth rank. Next is the Mediocre group, who usually manage to get promoted to the next class or level with average marks and, last of the lot are the Unfortunate ones, labelled as disinterested, incapable, incompetent, not serious, etc."

Then raising his voice to a higher pitch, Rahul said earnestly, "And what happens after that is even more serious. Everyone around these students live with these labels and treat them accordingly. The outstanding and clever students get importance at the cost of the rest of the students in the class."

The same parent again got up from his chair and asked bluntly, "So what's wrong with that? The outstanding and clever students have put in that extra effort in learning and hence we like them. I don't see anything wrong in this approach."

"Certainly, I'm not at all suggesting that the current approach is wrong, but when you have found out the reason/attributes of why clever students are so, can you share with me one reason, why the poorly performing students are so?"

The parent remained silent, perhaps he did not find an appropriate argument.

Rahul said, "Sir, you are silent, but the most experienced teacher in our school has labelled them as lazy, useless and *kamchor*, as the guy who doesn't want to work.

"Have you ever thought how cruel we are? How mean and, perhaps, insensitive we are? We fail to treat our own wards and children with dignity and, at most times, we even hurt their self-esteem!"

"I wish to put forward a psychological analysis of why certain students are not able to get marks as per the expectations of teachers and parents. Before that, I wish to convey some facts about all students, including those who get low marks.

"They are equal in intelligence and as capable as any other student in the class or school. Yet, despite their intelligence and capabilities, they are not able to make it to the expected performance standards – and we are to be blamed for this. I'm sure if we modify our approach and look at students with more empathy, we can make a big difference in their learning abilities, which in turn can impact their academic performance.

"Given a chance, even the student who has failed can get the highest marks in his class, provided we parents and teachers can guide him and rekindle his interest and enthusiasm, and give him confidence that he will be able to understand and do well in studies."

At this stage, the parent who had been raising objections, started clapping. Clapping continuously, he got up from his seat – followed by all the other parents in the auditorium. Madhuri's eyes moistened at the standing ovation, and as tears rolled down her cheeks, she did not bother to wipe them away. 'Let it flow, such emotional outbursts happen only once in our lifetime,' she told herself.

Pleased, Rahul waited for the applause to fade, for parents to sit down once again, and then proceeded, "I personally feel we are extremely unfair to our children, in that we have unreasonably high expectations from them. We expect outstanding performance from our children, but most of us fail to provide them a conducive environment and the support that is necessary for them to function well. Realizing this, I have taken up a challenge with the other teacher in our school that students who have scored disastrously low marks in earlier exams need to be guided and prepared in their studies, to that extent where they will score the highest marks or equivalent to that of the top performers of the school.

"Your wards, whose academic performance you must be aware of, have not been scoring the required marks in recent exams. I do not claim to have a magic wand that I will swish it and they will start demonstrating excellence in their academics, but I believe I know a method which can prepare these students for better academic performance, but it is not possible to implement it without your support and cooperation."

As Rahul paused for a moment, one parent got up from his seat, hesitatingly.

He folded his hands and said haltingly, "Sir, I'm Ramakrishnan, Murali's father. I am a poor man. I drive a rickshaw to support my family. I cannot talk on behalf of all, but as far as I'm concerned, I'm with you. It is fortunate that our children are in your batch. I'm sure with your magic touch, life will change for our kids. Please tell me what I need to do," he was trembling while addressing Rahul.

As Murali's father finished what he had to say, another parent stood up.

"Sir, I'm Ramesh Sonawane, Gautam's uncle. Due to Gautam's physical limitation, I'm very concerned about his future. Earlier, he used to do very well in school, and I was sure that he had a bright future ahead of him, but in the last couple of years, his academic performance has really gone down and that makes me anxious and worried. I run a small shop and live with limited means. In this competitive world, education is the best weapon to survive. If he does not study well, what will he do…. Particularly with his disablement. I will do whatever you tell me to do. But I'm not a very rich man, so I can't afford very high expenses."

Rahul smiled, "You don't need to spend any money; if required, I will incur the cost. I just need your assurance that you will support your wards. Give them your time and love. Give them the confidence that whatever happens you are with them, to support them at all times."

Then looking at the parents, Rahul assured them, "I'm not expecting any of you to spend money on your ward. I'm simply requesting you to give them your time and support in this critical moment of their lives. So far, they have not performed the way we all expect them to, so they have to swim against the tide, put in a lot of extra effort and I will ensure that they brighten up like shining stars.

"I'm going to start my schedule of special training from tomorrow morning at 7am, please be there on the school ground with your wards. We take off from there and start our journey towards excellence, for your wards and you too."

He paused for some time, thought over and added, "I understand that, you have your professions to take care, so give as much time as possible, perhaps every Sunday with your child. It would be good if you give more time, but at least try for every Sunday."

All parents looked quite charged up. The anxiety on their faces prior to the meeting was replaced with eagerness and confidence, which was visible in their walk as they left the auditorium. Madhuri couldn't move her eyes away from them. 'The way Rahul has transformed them in such a short time is effective leadership,' she thought.

I am too Busy a Parent

RAHUL AND AMEYA were waiting in the visitor's lounge of Mahajan Hospital. It was a big hospital in Andheri, reputed for its professionalism and treatment. At the same time, it was one of the most expensive hospitals too, and considered to be out of reach for the lower-middle class and poor section of the society.

As they waited in the lounge, Rahul quietly studied the place. The lounge was spread around 15,000sqft area, with an impressive front desk to welcome and guide visitors, patients and their relatives. Facing the front desk were multiple rows of seats for people to sit while they waited. Behind the front desk, there was an impressive artificial waterfall. The continuous soft murmur of the flowing water was refreshing and soothing. On the extreme right of the front desk was the OPD area, busy with the unending coming and going of patients and their attendants. On the extreme left side, there was the cafeteria; here too there was a constant stream of people moving in and out. Every time the door of the cafeteria opened, the aroma of food drew Rahul's attention towards it. He reminded himself that he was there for a specific purpose and would have to complete that work before he could treat his taste buds.

As he was thus thinking, a woman from the reception greeted him.

"Good morning, Mr Saxena. Sorry to keep you waiting. Dr Mahajan has arrived, he is in his chamber; he will meet you now."

The lady looked at Ameya, smiled and asked, "How are you, Ameya?"

"Fine."

Ameya's response, which sounded like a mechanical one, conveyed just the opposite.

Rahul and Ameya walked up to the chamber. Rahul knocked on the door and opened it.

"Hi, Rahul! I'm a lucky person that someone of your stature has walked into my hospital and found time to meet me," Amit welcomed him, gesturing at the chairs kept near his desk. Then Amit looked at Ameya and smiled, "Hi, son. Good to see you."

Rahul said as they sat down, "I must thank you once again, Amit, you treated my son a few months back."

Recalling that time when Sachin had been hospitalized, Dr Mahajan nodded, "Yes, yes, I remember. How is he now?"

"Better. He seems to be rising from the bottom of the improvement curve."

Unable to understand, Amit questioned him, "Bottom of the curve?"

"Let me explain."

Rahul got up from his chair, moved towards a white board hanging on the right-side wall, picked up the marker pen and drew a top facing, concave curve, like a cup open from the top.

He pointed at the curve, and made a mark on the top left hand of the curve, "Earlier, Sachin was here. Then there were some issues and we left him all alone. His performance started deteriorating and he came here," this time he marked a point at the bottom of the curve and then drew a line moving downwards from the top left of the curve and stopping at the bottom.

Looking at Amit, Rahul smiled, "Now I have taken on myself to extend all possible support for his journey towards the top of the curve again," then added, as he returned to his chair, "I've taken up the job of a teacher in his school. And not only for my son, but I'm working for your son's future as well."

Nodding his head, Amit grinned and remarked, "Oh, you are very sharp, Rahul!"

As he was speaking, there was a knock on the door, and the door opened to reveal a beautiful lady. Standing at the door, she poked her head inside the chamber, and asked if they would like to have something to drink.

"What would you like to have, Rahul?" asked Dr Mahajan.

"Green tea, please."

Then he looked at Ameya and asked him in Marathi, "*Tu kai ghenar* (What will you have)?"

"*Kai nako* (Nothing)," replied Ameya, with no interest in continuing the dialogue.

Amit told the lady to bring in two green teas and some biscuits; she nodded and withdrew.

"I'm sorry, Rahul, I got your invite but I couldn't attend the special session you had with parents," Amit said. "You see, I was busy in an operation. Every day, around 10–12 operations of various types are carried out in our hospital. These are booked well in advance, and it involves a lot of money – I'm sure you understand what I mean."

Rahul looked at Amit and asked, "How much?"

"Around ₹5 lakh, a day."

"I too am conducting an operation, the cost of it must be ₹10 lakh a day, multiplied by thirty, multiplied by 365; roughly ₹1,095 crore. And your presence is a must for this operation, otherwise it may fail."

Now Amit was curious, "What operation is this? It involves such a high figure, and yet my hospital doesn't even know about it. It's a great business opportunity," he immediately concluded.

"Amit, it is an operation to transform the lives of thirty students in the shortest possible time, and this operation also includes your own son, Ameya," Rahul informed him, quietly. "If this operation is successful, it will transform the lives of millions of students the world over."

"What do you want from me?"

"You are aware that Ameya is a student in my batch, and I have been entrusted with the responsibility to train and teach him so that he can overcome the difficulties he is facing in his studies, that he enjoys his studies, and performs to his potential. This can help him do well in current academics as well as in the future. By the way, you must be aware too, that he has not been doing well in his studies for the last couple of years?"

"Yes, I know," Dr Mahajan's face wore a grim look, and he glanced sternly at Ameya, who looked away, immediately. "But, surely you can see, how very busy I am. What can I do? Do you suggest that I give up running this big hospital and coach him at home?" he added with a bit of sarcasm.

As Amit was saying this, the hostess walked in, carrying a tray with tea and snacks. The discussion stopped for a while as tea was served. As she left, Rahul picked up a cup, took a sip and addressed the slightly annoyed doctor.

"He is poor in studies, that's a fact. But he was not born deficient of any capabilities that a normal child would possess but somehow the environment and the circumstances around him have made him what he is today. By the way, you are a doctor, you have all facilities to check Ameya and confirm if he has any mental disabilities? Does he suffer from any mental disabilities?" Rahul asked forcefully.

Amit remained silent, perhaps he did not know what to answer.

"Now the question is, do we allow him to continue like this and face uncertainties in his life or do we together do something and make him capable?"

Amit retorted loudly, particularly emphasizing Rahul's name, "You don't need to say all these things, *Mr Rahul Saxena*!" and then, added arrogantly, "I'm one of the biggest doctors of this city, I own one of the most modern and sophisticated hospitals in this city which itself is worth around ₹250 crore. My son will be inheriting all this… he will be able to lead his life without any tension. He doesn't need to care if he has studied or not."

Pressing his lips together, Dr Mahajan continued sarcastically, "I know your background, Mr Saxena. You were CEO of a very large and successful company. From what I have picked up from the media, you were making roughly US$ 10 mn per annum – that is roughly ₹60 crore a year. Don't you think you acted in haste and took up this poorly paid profession of teaching? What are you making now? A few lakhs a year," he ended dismissively.

Rahul realized Dr Mahajan was hopping mad, and was

becoming nastier by the minute. He addressed the incensed doctor just as formally, but politely and firmly.

"Money isn't everything in life, Amit. You are saying all this because you've never been on the verge of losing your son. I've seen it. I was about to lose my son, who attempted suicide... fortunately an unsuccessful attempt! When I sat beside his hospital bed, I realized how poor I was, despite having all the money that you mentioned just now. How poor I had made my son who had exhausted all options and tried to take his own life! Could he not have spoken to me at least once before taking such a drastic step, I had wondered. Then I realized, he had tried talking to me several times before taking that step, but I had closed all doors on his face. I had stopped communicating with him on some pretext or the other: of being very busy or not even finding the time to eat, so how could I give him time to listen to his story? Which, in my mind, was all supposedly crap!

"But after that incident, I realized that it was my mistake. He took that step and my life came to a grinding halt. Success, fame, money and career suddenly lost meaning for me. Then I realized my life is not in career, money and fame, it is in my son's well-being!"

Amit was listening to him attentively by now.

"And I'm not doing any favour to my son by becoming a teacher in his school – I'm fulfilling my responsibility. Now getting back to Ameya, my opinion is that he is a bright and nice boy, but maybe he is all alone. Not knowing whom to share his problems with, he is confused like most students of his age.

"We elders have neither the time nor the patience. If the student has a query in class, the teacher doesn't have the time to listen to him as he has to complete his syllabus, so he asks the student to say whatever he has to say quickly. When he is with parents like you, you have moneymaking avenues topmost in your mind, so you are extremely busy, you tell him to hurry up about it, quickly say what he has to say. And, most of the time, even before our child has explained his problem, our judgement is out! 'It's so simple and still you don't know?' or, '*Arrey*, you are supposed to know this,' or, 'What are/were you doing in the class?' So the best and safest thing for him is not to share his worries… at least, in that way, he is spared from criticism!

"Offering money and wealth to our children in exchange of our time and attention is the worst gift any parent could give to his/her ward; instead, we need to support them to be competent and capable. Give them the strength to believe that they have got the best support available in the form of parents and teachers. Give them the confidence and courage to face the challenges of life, take risks and chart their own path for the betterment of humanity. And you will see a different person growing from adolescent to manhood: smart, confident, and courageous with a strong foundation of love and character, with passion and enthusiasm to achieve big dreams, and bring glory to his country, family and teachers, like me…"

Rahul paused, controlled his emotions, smiled and said, "And then, one fine evening, somewhere around 15 years down the lane, I could telephone and ask you, 'Amit, what are we going to wear at Ameya's Nobel award ceremony?' Which son do you want, Dr Mahajan? A useless drunkard who is wasting and splurging his father's money or a hard-working scientist or technocrat aspiring for a Nobel prize, who will bring immense pride and joy to his parents, to his school and the nation as a whole. The choice is yours!

"But, I'm still going to insist that you spare some time for Ameya's well-being. Please join us in supporting him for the next couple of months and I can promise you that you will have a son who will support you for the rest of your life! I'm holding the first session with students and parents on Sunday, that is, tomorrow morning at seven sharp, in the school ground. Looking forward to seeing you there, Dr Mahajan."

There was deep silence in Dr Amit Mahajan's chamber. Amit felt for the first time in his life, that he had met a teacher who had the potential and desire to transform weak students. His taunting and dismissive expression was now replaced by one of respect and gratitude for Rahul. He looked at Ameya, walked towards his son and warmly embraced him.

Ameya looked at Rahul with thankful eyes.

*   *   *

It was a Saturday, 8.30am. Rahul was sitting in his staffroom in the school, and reading the newspaper, when there was a knock on the door. Rahul looked up; it was Shankar, nervous and hesitant.

Rahul smiled at him, "*Arrey*, Shankar, why are you standing there, come in."

With small steps, Shankar walked up to him, and said, "Sir, my mother has come to see you."

"Oh, where is she?" asked Rahul and hurriedly added, "is she waiting outside?"

"Yes, sir."

"Please bring her in."

Shankar went out and returned with a lady. Although Rahul had met her once briefly when he had fought with Dagdu Dada in the slum where they stayed, he hadn't seen her clearly in the

175

dimly lit surroundings. Rahul observed her now. In her late thirties, Shankar's mother was a heavily built woman of medium height. Fair complexioned, her prominent nose and large eyes made her look somewhat fierce. As she entered the room, she looked confident.

She folded her hands and said, "Namaste, sir."

"Namaste, sister. Please sit down," Rahul's voice was soft and gentle.

She sat down and the chair creaked under her weight.

"Perhaps, this is because of my weight," she joked.

Rahul smiled, "Good you came to our school. Have you come here before?"

"No, this is the first time I have ever visited any school."

"Sorry, I couldn't get you," Rahul was confused.

"Sir, *bachpan mein main bahut husiyar thi* (as a kid I was very bright), but in my childhood I could never go to school as I used to work on farm land to support my poor father.

"If I had gone to school, there would be no one to support my family: my parents and we eight siblings. At that time, my parents and I would work the whole day in the farm, and in exchange, we used to get grains, which we would cook for the family. The day there was no work in the farm, we would sleep empty stomach. But I want my son to do well in his studies, so I've come to take your advice," she stopped, and added, folding her hands and with sudden tears, "that night you fought bravely and saved my son from his shameless father and the tentacles of Dagdu Dada. I'm really grateful to you for your act, which has helped save Shankar's future."

As she was speaking, Rahul observed that her two front teeth were missing. She also looked older than her actual age, perhaps because of the hardships she must have gone through, and was still going through. But she was smiling a lot, which indicated her innocent nature and large heart.

She continued, "Shankar told me about the challenge you have taken to support poor students like him and make them shine in their coming exams so that they can do well in studies and become a great man like you, some day in the future," her eyes sparkled as she said this, and then quickly added, grinning, "I have seen you on TV. Your interview and the award function. Of course, I didn't understand much but I saw you on TV. Shankar told me that you are his classmate Sachin's father."

Rahul simply smiled.

"Shankar's father did not come with you?"

"Oh that drunkard, does he have any sense for worldly or family matters? He is just busy drinking and when he is free from that, he demands money from me and if I don't give him, he gets busy in beating me."

She told Rahul sadly, who could feel the pain in her voice.

He said, "I see you are quite keen that Shankar learns and becomes a person to reckon with. Until then, you will have to support him. I know you can't teach him; that we will do here but you will have to ensure that he is not bothered by your husband and other trouble-makers like Dagdu Dada. If he is being bothered, you will inform me immediately."

He paused for some time, looked at her, and then added, "Can you do that?"

She replied in the affirmative.

Work Together, Build Together

IT WAS A Sunday evening, around 5pm. As the day progressed, and the sun continued its westward journey, it became cooler. While Rahul sat on a bench placed below a tree, students and their parents sat together, as usual, in twos or threes, for joint studies.

Suddenly, a loud voice of someone shouting shattered the peace and quiet that had enveloped the study groups. Rahul looked around: Dr Amit Mahajan was berating Ameya.

"How many times do I have to teach you the same topic? You still haven't understood! What's wrong with you? Do you think I have the time to repeat it a hundred times? Wake up, Ameya, wake up! You are so stupid, even a dumb person will be better than you!" and so continued the ridicule and angry outburst.

Ameya, his head down, silently listened to his father's scolding; his body language was that of one who was miserable.

Suddenly seeing Rahul striding towards them, Amit started complaining, "Rahul, I'm tired. I've been teaching him the same topic for such a long time, and still he hasn't got it in his head! It's ridiculous."

Rahul smiled and chanted, *"Hari no marag chhe shura no, nahi kayar nu kaam jo ne, partham pahela mastak muki vadti levu naam jone."*

Amit looked confused, "What did you say, Rahul?"

Rahul smiled again and explained, "This is a Gujarati song. It means that the path to God is full of difficulties and challenges. It is not within the capacity of weak-minded people to achieve it. You need to forget about your own self and work towards realizing God. In our context, the path of excellence demands tremendous courage and determination; it is not everyone's cup of tea. That's exactly the reason why our society has only a handful of great people who can be counted on finger tips and not in hundreds or thousands.

"Today you have perhaps done the greatest damage to your son by taking out your frustration on him, giving him all the negative messages that you could. I'm surprised you did that because, from what I understand, of all operations, heart surgeries are the most delicate as doctors have to take every measure to ensure that when they are operating the heart, the arteries and veins do not get damaged. Am I right?"

"Yes absolutely," Amit replied.

Here, Ameya, seeing his father distracted, got a chance to sneak away, to a group of his batch mates, who were taking a break from studies.

Rahul carried on with what he had been saying, Amit listening to him with undivided attention, "Then how come a heart specialist like you punctured the heart of a young boy, so ruthlessly? Just look at his face, look into his eyes… is he the same boy whom you love so much? Then how can you shake his confidence through such harsh words?" Rahul questioned Amit a bit angrily.

But he immediately controlled himself, and spoke to the doctor in a softer voice, "Amit, my dear friend, I want to share with you my own experience when I was in the ninth standard. I wasn't good in mathematics. I had got only 24 marks out of 80 in mathematics in the prelim exams that year, which means I had failed in maths. I was terribly upset and cried a lot in front of my father. My father took me to one teacher who he knew well. He listened to me carefully, and then he asked me to take tuition from him every day for an hour. I went to his house on the same day because I wanted to overcome my weakness as quickly as possible.

"I still remember my first day at his place. While entering his house, my confidence was at its lowest, thanks to my teacher in school whose choice of words had convinced me that I was no good. Plus, my mark sheet validated what my teacher had said! When I reached this maths tutor's house, he welcomed me with a lot of love and warmth, introduced me to his family members. Then he asked me 'So you are finding mathematics difficult?'

"I nodded my head in affirmation. He just smiled at me."

Rahul gazed at the distance, as if he was trying to look into his past, recalling the incident. He continued, "I'll never forget that smile. He asked me two or three simple questions related to mathematics; at first I was surprised by the simplicity of the questions, so I answered them quickly. He congratulated me for answering those easy questions. Not only did he appreciate me, but his family members too congratulated me!

"I thought he was only pretending, but later when I grew up, I realized that at the subconscious level, that first congratulation had set the foundation for my future self-confidence. Then he started teaching me the subject. With that foundation of self-confidence, which he had established on the first day, my attitude towards mathematics had changed slightly. It had changed from 'I can't do' to 'I can try', and 'perhaps do'!

"Now, after so many years, when I look back, I realize that I just couldn't understand the concepts and theorems in the first month, but never ever did my tutor lose his temper, never did he use any word or action that could have negatively impacted my confidence. He was very patient with me while teaching. He would teach the lesson and ask me questions on it. Initially, I floundered, but he explained the concepts patiently, ensuring that I understood it from the root. As I started understanding the theories, I was able to pick up and learn the subject faster and the quality of my answers started improving. For every wrong answer, there was more effort from his side, but for every right answer, I was handsomely praised.

"Now when I think of that process and analyse it, I realize he was playing a psychological game of praise, which triggered my interest and enthusiasm. This positive energy of praise (acceptance) along with enthusiasm (affirmation) started reinforcing confidence (belief) in me. Then I reached a stage where, for every question he would ask, I would expect a praise. This worked at a subconscious level. Since I wanted him to praise me, I needed to give the correct answer, which means I had to work hard, which I did happily!

"After two to three months, I developed a different approach. Since praise was necessary for every question, I started asking him in advance what he would be teaching me the next day. I would read that chapter and go for my tuition class well prepared. Better preparations resulted in more compliments, which means, there was more acceptance, greater positive energy and higher confidence reinforcement. He would give me more and more problems to solve.

"Earlier, I would take a long time to solve the problems, but now, since I found the subject interesting, I was able to solve the same problems in far lesser time. Slowly and steadily, my fear of mathematics vanished and was replaced by my liking for the subject. As a child, I didn't notice this change apparently. But, his efforts and conscious approach had taken me to such mental readiness, that the subject that I had always wanted to avoid, now became my favourite subject!

"My performance in school started to improve, which amazed even my mathematics teacher. He too was very happy with this improvement. So he too started appreciating my performance, which boosted my confidence further."

Rahul paused and looked at Amit and said, "Can you guess how I had fared in the final exams?"

Amit shook his head.

"I scored 82 out of 100 in the final exams. But more than that, this exercise had rekindled my interest in mathematics. I fared better and better year after year, with the result that I studied engineering, which demands higher proficiency in mathematics.

"I firmly believe that all children are equal with similar learning capabilities. The difference that we observe among students' performances, majorly depends on two factors. First, the environment in which the student is growing up, whether it is conducive and relaxing for studies or otherwise. Generally, the environment at the early ages of a student, say up to the third or fourth class, is highly conducive. After which, parents', teachers', and relatives' high expectations turn the environment into just the opposite!

"Second, but most important, how deeply has the student understood the subject and the associated logic. In other words, whether the student has an in-depth understanding of the subject."

Thrusting his hands in his trouser pocket, Rahul glanced at Amit squarely and pointed out, "Parents like you have no time for their wards, so children are left to teachers. Teachers put in their best efforts at school, but for one teacher – who also has to complete the syllabus – it is not possible to give personal attention to each and every student in the class. Plus, there are naughty students in the class, who disturb everyone, and this takes a toll on the teacher's energy and time. He has to control them, and also complete the day's lesson.

"Naturally then, teachers tend to become tough and, at times, inaccessible. So while the teacher is teaching, the mischievous ones miss out on what is being taught. Then, there are some who did pay attention, but couldn't understand the lesson fully; they should have asked questions and got their doubts cleared, but they remain silent. All these factors create gaps in a child's expected learning vs actual learning. It is this gap which is the measure of dumbness, in your own words, of any student; the larger the gap, the dumber is the student!"

Amit was listening to him attentively, keenly, as if he wanted to grab every word.

He thought for some time and asked, "Rahul, in that case, how do we remove or reduce the learning gap?"

"Amit, you have asked a very valid question. It's doable, but needs a lot of patience and perseverance on the tutor's side. First, the environment surrounding the child needs correction. All discouraging or negative words like 'you are dumb', 'you will never learn in life', should be avoided. The *child is not a dustbin where you can dump all your frustrations.* Empowering gestures such as expressions of love and caress will boost his level of confidence. This can be done by cheerfully encouraging his every effort; appreciating his every success – it'll enthuse him to do better; shower love on him; and don't criticize or ridicule him when he makes a mistake, Amit. Where academics are concerned, revise the easier chapters first, check if his fundamental knowledge is strong and, if needed, repeat until he has fully understood the chapter. Ask questions. Begin with simple questions first, slowly build on the complexity of questions. At any point of time, if he is confused, discuss what could be the answer. The mantra, Amit, should be 'Work Together, Build Together': a positive environment, enthusiasm, confidence and subject matter interest. Just work on these, and you will be amazed with the results!" concluded Rahul confidently.

Realizing his mistake, Amit sighed glumly, "How much damage I have done to my own son!"

He looked around and called loudly, "Ameya, Ameya, where are you?"

Ameya came out of a group of students, and walked towards his dad.

As Amit ran towards him, Ameya stopped, and shouted aloud, "Dad, *nako*."

Thinking that his father was running towards him to grab and punish him, Ameya took to his heels. Rahul laughed heartily at this funny scene. Amit wanted to embrace Ameya, while the son, afraid that his father would spank him, was running away from him!

Dad, You Interfere too Much

"SACHIN! IT'S ALMOST 2 hours that you've been watching TV. You need to control your TV time and do some physical activities!" scolded Rahul, while entering the drawing room.

Sachin was busy watching his favourite programme, so he didn't react, his eyes glued to the TV set.

"This guy will spoil his eyes, why won't he do some physical activities? At least he can go out and spend time with friends or play some game," murmured a worried Rahul.

He came close to Sachin, picked up the remote and switched off the TV set. Sachin got very upset.

"Why did you switch off the TV, Dad? I was watching my favourite programme!"

"Yes, I know. You've been watching all your favourite programmes for the last 2 hours. Whereas, the doctor has advised you against watching too much TV, remember?" Rahul told him sternly.

"Yes, I do remember. But you should not switch off the TV abruptly in this way."

"Then how do I switch it off?"

Folding his hands, and with his head bowed down, Rahul moved towards Sachin in a dramatic way and grinned, "Should I offer some *stuti? Shri Sachina, Shri Sachina. Me tula karto prarthana. Kara band* TV *aani karo krupa* on me."

Sachin forgot his anger and started laughing.

"Yes, that would be great! Every time you want me to switch off the TV, please submit your request in this way," then suddenly added, "I don't understand, what do you lose if I watch TV for a longer time? Are you worried about the electricity bill?" Sachin asked his father anxiously.

Rahul looked at Sachin and replied, "No, I'm not concerned about the electricity bill; I'm worried about your health and well-being."

Sachin could not understand so he stared back at his father questioningly.

"Let me explain," said Rahul as he sat down beside Sachin, on the sofa. "TV is a good medium for entertainment and information. But it has got some negative features too: excess TV viewing could impact your cognitive/learning skills, sleeping patterns and also cause obesity. If it is not controlled at your age, it can make you vulnerable to diseases such as hypertension, diabetes or insomnia when you grow up."

Sachin, on his part, stared at Rahul with disbelief. Rahul moved near him, took his hand in his palms and caressed it.

"See, as your father, I'm constantly worried about your well-being. You are young right now and so, your knowledge or understanding of life is limited. I have learnt a lot many things through my own experiences, which are generally a result of pain and sufferings, learnt the hard way. That is why, I intend to guide you so that you don't have to go through similar experiences or difficulties.

"Let me give you an example. I have told you many times to keep your important things and documents in its right or proper place, so that you can find them at a moment's notice. There is a reason why I keep insisting on this, and I'll tell you why now.

"I was in the tenth standard, and on the very first day of the exam itself, when I reached the examination centre, the invigilators wanted to see my admit card. I searched my pockets, where I had kept it, but could not find it. I realized I had left it elsewhere, may be at home or, worse, I had dropped it on the way somewhere. On not being able to show the admit card, he refused to allow me to appear for the exam. I pleaded a lot but he didn't budge.

"I was frightened because if I couldn't sit for the exam, one year in my life would be wasted. Not knowing what to do, I started crying. I cried for almost half an hour, but for him a rule was a rule. Those days there were no mobiles; even the place we used to stay in didn't have any phone nearby. There was one in a local baniya's place, but I had never bothered to carry his phone number.

"Fortunately for me, that day my school's principal visited the centre and he found me crying. He asked me the reason and requested the centre authorities to allow me to write the exam. After a lot of persuasion, they agreed and I was allowed to sit for the exam. That day, when I reached home, I found the admit card in my school bag. A small piece of document, but very important which could have spoiled my one full year!

"That experience taught me a lot! That's why, whenever you deal with important papers and your exams or any other important matter, I just can't stop myself from telling you to take care of your papers, keep them at an appropriate place. This advice is mostly unsolicited, I know, but still my love and care for you forces me to give it to you anyway.

"I know you don't like it, but I don't want you to suffer the same bitter experience that I had suffered in the past! This is not true only for me, but for every father. What you guys perceive as an interference, is in reality a concern for your well-being. This is a sort of misunderstanding, between parents and their wards, wherein parents want to protect their wards from all sorts of difficulties, but children consider it as an interference and object or resist!

"I can give you several examples of very powerful and intelligent people, who are greatly respected outside their homes, no one would even dare raise a voice against them. But, they are helpless where their own children are concerned. More often than not, their advice is misunderstood by their own kids, and sometimes they even have to face insults, at times in front of even outsiders!"

Seeing Rahul getting upset, Sachin, who could not bear to see his father like this, hugged him and said, "I'm sorry, Dad. I didn't want to hurt you. My feeling is that now that I have grown up, why do you worry when I can take care of myself?"

Patting him lovingly, Rahul smiled, "I feel proud when you tell me this. But still, like most parents, I will continue to guide and advice you out of my unconditional love for you. We parents often overlook the fact that growing children feel they are capable of taking care of themselves."

He lightly ran his fingers through Sachin's hair.

"Your grandmother used to worry about me even after I had joined Gold Star. Every day, when I would leave for office, she would wait near the car. While saying bye to me, almost every time she used to ask me if I had carried my wallet. Then, she would say 'drive carefully', 'don't quarrel with anyone', and 'most importantly eat your food on time'. Initially, I did not like it, and a couple of times I had an argument with her; sometimes I spoke rudely to her. But, that didn't deter her!

"I used to wonder at that time, why does she keep saying the same thing, or advising me almost every day? But I could understand her feelings only after your birth. I could relate with those feelings, when I started developing similar feelings for you!

"There is another reason why parents continue to advise their kids. You are now an adolescent, you are not matured enough to take independent decisions. And hence, your decisions/actions are generally influenced by people/situations around you. Now, this influence can be positive or negative. Positive influences are always good to have, like Mahatma Gandhi."

Rahul paused for some time. Hearing Mahatma Gandhi's name, Sachin became attentive.

"He developed the habit of speaking the truth after watching a drama on Raja Harish Chandra. Generally, all parents want their children to adopt positive influences, like Mahatma Gandhi did, but often reality is just the opposite. Under the influence of peers or perceived role models, youngsters sometimes pick up habits such as smoking, even drugs, or other serious vices at this age. This happens because you guys are very emotional and tender at this age. A small trigger and an adolescent can go off-track in no time. Constant advice by parents, teachers and other well-wishers act like brakes in a car. It offers resistance to your thoughts, makes you think and often stops you from taking a wrong path."

Sachin hugged him again, "Sorry, Dad. I misunderstood you, as nagging me all the time! I'm thankful to have a father like you. Now I understand why you also give so much importance to physical fitness and sports even in your daily routine. I promise you, Dad, I will not only follow your instructions, however hard they may be, but also imbibe them in my life."

Then he jumped up and put his arms around Rahul's neck. Rahul stretched out his hands and took him in his arms.

At this, Sachin said gleefully, "Like this, you will never allow me to fall. So your suggestions are not interferences but a short cut to my successful life."

Father and son tightly hugged each other, the warmth of love enveloping them.

My Father's True Lies

IT WAS TUESDAY. The bell rang, signifying the change of period. Madhuri entered the class.

"Good afternoon, ma'am!" the students greeted Madhuri.

"Good afternoon, children!" she responded with a wide smile on her face.

"Children, today, for our social science class, I'm going to give you a topic on which all of you have to speak. Since we have a limitation on the number of students who can speak, I will select three students who will talk on the topic in the next class.

"Today we are going to discuss about a very important person in our life – Father. He is the pillar of our family. He provides security and protection to all of us. Now I want all of you to think and speak for about 5 minutes about your own father in front of the class tomorrow. Are you all ready?"

This being a new experiment, the students grew excited about it. Madhuri opened a book that she was holding in her hands, and took up another topic and taught the children for about 30 minutes, after which she left for her next class, when the bell rang.

Murali Ramakrishnan, one of the boys in the class, was in deep thought, after she left. And, it continued even during recess. Usually, he played with his classmates but he was aloof that day, and kept to himself, sitting in a corner.

After school was over, his father came to pick him up. Murali greeted and hugged him but remained silent all the way back home. There, too, he preferred to keep away from his family, and even turned a deaf ear when his sister and brother asked him to join them and the other kids in the playground. His mother, however, had noticed his unusual behaviour and, that night when he was about to turn in, she asked him if something was wrong.

He answered in the negative, and only asked, "Mum, why does Father lie so much?"

Angry, his mother spoke sharply, "What nonsense? You have one of the best fathers in the world; he never lies. What's wrong with you? Is this what you learn in school?"

Murali didn't reply, just turned his back towards his mother and closed his eyes.

Next day, he got up later than usual. Yet, he felt like sleeping some more, but his mother woke him up as he was getting late for school. He got up and sat cross-legged on his mattress for some time, rubbing his eyes, yawning; and looked around. They had a small house, just one room. 'Too small for five people,' he thought. 'I don't know why we have such a small house while some of my friends like Sachin and Sapna, have such big houses. You can play football inside their house,' he mused. Still sitting, he gazed at the walls; they were all dull; in some places, the paint had come off, while molds were growing in patches in other portions because of seepage. Overall, these looked like the face of an ugly, old woman! He then looked at the 'kitchen'. There was no separate kitchen as such: a corner of the house served as the kitchen where his mother cooked their meals and packed tiffin for all of them.

'Mother,' Murali's thoughts shifted to his mother. He stared at her. 'Mother is really pretty, but she looks weak and pale,' he thought sadly. As if on cue, questions surfaced to his mind: 'why can't she have a glowing face like the mothers of my rich friends? Why does she always give me such simple lunch for my tiffin? Just see what Sachin gets for his tiffin – some times it's noodles, some day's it's pasta, sandwiches, or sweets!' Murali started salivating just thinking about Sachin's tiffin…

'Oh my God, I haven't brushed my teeth yet!' Murali thought, his eyes widening in dismay, 'if Mother notices it, she will scold me.' Again, his mind drifted to various thoughts: 'Mother is loving but very strict. She never tolerates any indiscipline or lethargy.' He got up from his mattress, rolled it and kept it on a table. There were many such 'beds', one for each member of the family, lying on that table.

He got ready for school, and sat down on the floor, beside his siblings and his father for breakfast. His mother was serving food, while the others sat in a row.

"What's for breakfast today?" Murali asked his mother.

This was his daily habit; he would ask her the same question when he sat down for his meals. His mother remained silent; perhaps she didn't like the question.

His father replied, "Your favourite… Aloo Parantha and a glass full of milk. How do you like it?"

A huge smile lit up Murali's face, and he exclaimed, "Wow! Great," and then added joyfully, "I will eat three paranthas today."

His mother gave him a look, but his father replied, "Eat as many as you like, my son."

"Sure? Will it not fall short?"

"No, son. Food will never be short for any of you," his father replied, glanced at his mother and added, "And neither for your mother."

As Murali started eating his breakfast, he saw his mother gesture something, which he didn't understand.

Abruptly, his father asked, "I think these paranthas are too spicy for me. Can you give me something which is less spicy?"

In a very low voice she replied, "Would you like to eat the Khichdi I made last night?"

"Oh yes. I would love it," Murali's father said hastily.

She served him a plateful of Khichdi and took away one parantha from his plate, and placed it on Murali's younger brother's plate. Then, taking some of the Khichdi on another plate, remarked, "Yesterday's Khichdi was quite good. I also feel like having it."

They finished breakfast, and left for school. Murali and his siblings got into the auto – his father, who was an auto driver by profession, drove them to school.

After a while, Murali blurted out, "Are we poor, Father?"

His father was startled, but maintained a smile on his face, and replied, "No, my son, we are not poor. Why do you ask? God has given us whatever we need," then he asked thoughtfully, "why are you asking? Did anyone tell you anything?"

"No, just asking."

As the auto sped towards school, Murali looked unseeingly at the passing shops, trees and the road. Once again in deep thought, the noise of the auto rickshaw's engine failed to distract him.

★   ★   ★

Madhuri entered the class. All the students were busy talking amongst themselves, as today was an important day for them. Madhuri Ma'am would be asking a few of them to speak about their father. The children were discussing and guessing who would be asked to speak.

The usually active and talkative Murali was quietly sitting on the bench. He seemed confused. Madhuri noticed that Murali had not realized that she had entered their class.

She shushed them to quieten down, looked at the whole class and asked cheerfully, "You all remember, I hope, what we will be discussing today?"

"Yes, ma'am!" her students responded enthusiastically.

Madhuri smiled at Sapna and said, "Sapna, let's start with you, come forward and speak about your father."

Sapna made her way to the front of the class, and faced her classmates. The children settled down quickly, and at a sign from her teacher, she started her short speech.

"Good morning, ma'am and friends. I'm very happy that Ma'am has given me an opportunity to speak about my father. His name is Sunil Pradhan. He is the MLA of our locality and a very popular leader. My father loves me very much. He takes me out on weekends and gets me all that I want.

"One day when I was sick, my father remained by my bedside through the night to take care of me. When I recovered, he took me along with him, on a pilgrimage to Shirdi, to Sai Baba's temple. I really enjoy his company and like to play chess with him. He is a master in chess and I have never won any match with him so far.

"I love my father and I'm proud of him. Thank you."

Madhuri said to the beaming girl, "Good, Sapna. You may take your seat."

As Sapna went back happily to her seat, Madhuri looked at Murali and asked, "Any trouble, Murali? Are you all right?"

"Yes, ma'am. Everything's all right."

"Then why do you look so puzzled?"

"Nothing, ma'am. I'm just wondering about my father."

"Do you want to talk about your father? Why don't you come here and talk?"

Murali came forward, and turned towards the class.

"Friends," began Murali, "I love my father. He is very good, always smiling and takes good care of me. There has rarely been a situation when I have asked for something, and he has not given it to me. Sometimes, if he is unwilling to give me the thing that I have asked for, then I know it is only because it won't be good for me. My father drives an auto rickshaw. Sometimes, many students have laughed at me and ridiculed me as my father is a poor man. But I don't care about what others think of him. I know he is the best person in this world.

"But, there's one thing that always puzzles me about my father. He lies to me a lot."

He paused, and looked at Madhuri, who was shocked at this statement. At first, she couldn't believe his words, and stared back at him in disbelief.

Murali continued, "Yes, he lies to me a lot. Just this morning, Mother had made Aloo Paranthas for breakfast. I like paranthas, so I said I would eat to my capacity. He smiled and asked me to go ahead, that I could eat as many paranthas as I like, but after a few seconds, instead of eating the paranthas that were on his plate, he said these were too spicy, and asked for Khichdi instead.

"I know he likes paranthas, and he is strong so he can eat more spicy food than I can, but still he did not eat paranthas. Isn't it

196

lying?" slowly Murali grew emotional, his voice started trembling.

"I can give several such examples. One Sunday, I wanted to have an ice cream. And because I like an ice-cream parlour in Andheri which I had visited along with Sachin and Rahul Sir earlier, I insisted that my father take me to the same parlour. All three of us, my brother, sister and I sat in our auto, and my father drove. I was impatient, and urged him to hurry to the ice-cream parlour, and take a shorter route. Initially, he refused as it was a one-way, but on my insistence, he took that route. At the end of that road stood a traffic policeman, who stopped our auto and asked to see his license. Which Father showed. Then he questioned Father, why was he driving in the wrong direction on a one-way road? Father explained that, it was his mistake, as he did not notice the one-way sign at the beginning of the lane. He begged to be forgiven for his mistake and be allowed to proceed. The policeman asked Father to move out of the auto rickshaw and follow him. Father stepped out of the auto, and went along with him. When he returned after some time, Father said he wouldn't be able to buy us any ice cream as he didn't have any money…. How is it possible? Isn't it lying? Some time back when we started, he had money, then how come he suddenly lost his money?" by now Murali's eyes were full of tears.

"I love food and love to go out to restaurants. Whenever we go out, Father says he is not hungry. Despite my repeated pleas, he refuses to eat, saying that restaurant food doesn't suit him. Is it possible? I know he is lying to me there too.

"Clothes… he wears the same set of clothes for years together, but gets us new ones. He has only one pair of sandals which he wears everywhere, but I have three pairs of shoes.

When I ask him to get a new pair for himself, he teases me, saying I am his Collector son so I need to live in style. I call this behaviour of his as cheating! How many sacrifices will he make for us? Why is it that he only has to make sacrifices without even giving me a chance to sacrifice at least one thing for him, isn't it cheating?"

There was pin drop silence in the class. Everyone was stunned and deeply moved.

"But still I love my father, despite the fact that he fools me many times. Because I know, he is cheating on me for my future. He is working hard to give me a life that will be full of comfort. I wish all of you had the privilege of having a cheater father. Thank you."

Numb at this revelation, Madhuri didn't know when Murali finished talking about his father – and who spoke next about his/her father. It appeared to her that the whole world had stopped for some time. Suddenly, the piercing sound of the school bell rang out, signifying that school was over for that day – but still no one was in a hurry to get up and run. Mechanically, Madhuri picked up her books and left the class.

Help Me with my Memory

STRETCHED OUT ON the sofa, Rahul was relaxing after the long hours at school. After a while, it struck him that Sachin was behaving strangely. He was walking from one room to the other continuously, and Rahul realized that this strolling from room to room had been going on for quite some time. Sachin would come to the room, as if he wanted to share something with Rahul, but stop at the door itself and then turn back without entering or saying anything.

After Sachin had repeated this for about the fifth time, Rahul called out, "Hello Sachin, beta! All okay?"

Sachin replied in a low voice, "Fine, Dad. Hope you are fine, too."

"Yes, I'm always fine. But you don't seem to be doing fine. What's troubling you?"

"Nothing serious."

"So there is something which is troubling you and it is not

serious. Fine, then, we needn't go to the hospital and admit you there!" Rahul said jokingly.

Sachin said in a surly voice, "It's PJ."

"What's PJ?"

"*Pakau* joke."

Rahul wanted to cheer him up, so he continued teasing Sachin.

"Okay, in that case, can I tell you a better joke?"

"No, Dad. I don't want to listen to any joke, I'm not in a good mood."

"Then I will sing for you, son."

"No, Dad. No song."

"No joke. No song. Then what do you want? Are you in some trouble? Is there something I can do to help you?"

"No, Dad, seriously, even you can't help me in this."

"No, I will help you without becoming serious. So tell me."

"Dad.... My memory," said Sachin hesitantly.

"What about it?" asked Rahul.

"Nothing, I just wanted to know what to do if I have a poor memory."

Rahul continued teasingly, "Do you mean to say some friend of yours has forgotten you? Tell me, is it a boyfriend or a girlfriend? Simply call your friend, talk to him and jog his memory! Why do you worry?"

Now Sachin was becoming restless and said in hurry, "I'm not talking about somebody else's memory – I'm talking about my own memory, so that I'll be able to quickly recall what I have read or studied."

Rahul had understood Sachin's question at the first instance itself but he was kidding with the boy to make him smile, which did not happen; Sachin continued the whole conversation with a tensed face.

"So you feel you do not have a good memory. Hmm, is that what you think and believe?" asked Rahul.

"Yes. What do I do to improve my memory? Please help me."

"Fine, Sachin, I will tell you whatever I know of improving your memory, but before that, let's go out and chill in some open area. I'm getting bored here."

Sachin was very happy with this proposal, and immediately agreed, "That's a great idea, Dad. Where shall we go, Dad?"

"Wellington's Club or Juhu Sea Beach. You choose."

"Juhu Beach. I'll go for a horse ride there."

"Okay, but on one condition. You'll wear your blue jeans."

Sachin was surprised at his dad's condition, but since he was in a hurry to get ready and go for the outing, he didn't argue. He simply agreed, and complied.

After another 15 minutes, the father–son duo was ready. On Sachin's insistence, Rahul took out the Lamborghini Veneno and set out for a drive. Sachin, seating beside Rahul, was still in deep thought.

"What are you thinking about, son?"

"Memory! How can I develop such a memory, that I read something once and remember everything! Dad, is it possible? Unfortunately, my memory is not like yours!"

"Do you think I have a good memory?"

"Yes, absolutely. You remember everything so well. That itself is proof that you have a good memory."

"Okay, let me ask you a few questions. Are you ready?"

"Oh no, Dad! No questions, we are out to have fun."

"I'll ask you only on cricket."

"Oh, that's great. I'm ready," said Sachin excitedly.

"Tell me, in which year did India play its first Test Cricket?"

Sachin promptly replied, "India played its first cricket Test Match against England in 1932. England won the match by 158 runs."

"In which year did India win its first world cup? Under whose captaincy?"

Sachin answered, "In 1983. India won its first world cup under Kapil Dev."

"Good! Sachin, you have very good knowledge of cricket. Now, let's talk of something else," Rahul tried to change the topic but Sachin was not keen.

"Dad, it's really interesting, please ask me some more questions and I promise to answer all of them correctly."

Rahul started teasing him, "But sometime back you told me you are tired and you want to relax, so let me not bother you with questions on cricket. It's not fair on my part to bother a tired person."

"No, Dad, it's okay."

"Sachin, I'm not ready with any more questions on cricket, so I'll prepare some new questions and ask you. I should also be ready with answers to judge whether your replies are correct or not."

Sachin started laughing, "Dad... about cricket my answers would always be correct. Don't you worry, Dad!"

By this time, they had reached the entrance of a park. Rahul parked the car and they started walking in the park. Rahul chose a bench from where there was a good view of the sea. Rahul sat on the bench and asked Sachin to sit down, beside him.

Looking at the sun, which was setting in the west, Rahul said, "Sometime back, you were asking me about memory and how to make one's memory more powerful. Right?"

Sachin replied in affirmation.

"My son! A few moments back, I did a quick test of your memory and I can say with absolute confidence that you have an excellent memory. Just look how effortlessly you answered all my questions about cricket! Most of the events had happened when you were not even born! Yet, you knew the correct answers with years and dates for all the events; that means you are not suffering from any mental disorder that can be diagnosed as memory inadequacy."

"Then how come I don't remember things I study as well as I remember things and events about cricket?"

Rahul smiled at him, "You replied sometime back."

"Really? When? I don't remember," now it was Sachin's turn to be surprised. 'How come I've answered questions and still don't know,' he thought.

"Okay, let me remind you. When we sat in the car and I told you that I'll ask you some questions, your immediate response was 'Dad, we are out to have fun', right? Just think... and tell me why did you say that?"

"Oh, Dad, I thought you were going to ask me questions on science or mathematics. That's why I reacted like that."

"But when I started asking you questions on cricket, you were very enthusiastic. And when I stopped asking questions, you said you were enjoying them so I should ask you some more questions, right?" Rahul added.

Sachin nodded his head in affirmation.

"My son, your reaction to two different subjects, that is, mathematics or science and cricket was very different. Therefore, in your mind, your liking for these two subjects is far different.

Whenever the topic is cricket, your reaction and hence mental readiness about that subject is very positive. That shows your keen interest in cricket. That is why you are very receptive towards any information/discussion on cricket. And hence, you remember whatever you've read or come across on cricket."

Rahul looked at Sachin who was listening attentively.

"But when it comes to studies, say, mathematics or science, your mental readiness is not naturally positive, you have to push yourself for the same. If I analyse your mental state correctly, you show a bit of reluctance towards your studies subconsciously. That is one reason why your memory recall on studies is not as good as your recall on cricket."

Now, Sachin was becoming interested in the discussion, and he asked, "What is the other reason?"

Rahul looked pleased with his question, "Now you are getting on the track, son. The other reason is your subject mastery. You must have heard the famous proverb 'Success breeds success', which means your interest and willingness to work on a particular subject increases when you envisage higher chances of perceived success. In order to develop mastery on any subject, you must first like it genuinely."

"Dad, that's fine but how do I ensure that I like a particular subject genuinely? Many a times I find it boring, let's say… physics."

"There are multiple steps through which you can develop a genuine liking for a particular subject. The first is to see the relevance of that subject in your life, that is, how that subject is helping or going to help you currently as well as in the future. If you think of physics, it has enormous utility in our day-to-day life. We use electricity every day – the movement of cars; the

Radio Frequency signals through which our mobiles work; computers; and how your games work. All these things have physics in its base."

Rahul continued when he saw Sachin was listening attentively.

"The next step is to see your own self-interest. See the bigger picture. Dream a big picture for your life, what you want to become. How can these subjects, say, learning physics or mathematics, help you in achieving your big dreams? Think of it daily. A day will come when you will have developed an affinity for these subjects which can help you accomplish your bigger dream, like all great people. Let us take an example of a great actor of our times, Amitabh Bachchan, or cricket legend Sachin Tendulkar. They have all achieved greatness through continued affinity for their subject matter and by continuously striving towards excellence."

"What next, Dad?" asked Sachin curiously.

"The next step is to understand it fully. Pay full attention to every small detail about the subject; learn more about it from all sources, what you learn in class could be the first source. Come home and revise what you have learnt in class. If it is mathematics, solve more and more problems, initially with the help of your teacher and later all by yourself. Start with easy sums first, slowly moving towards more complex ones. Praise yourself for every success.

"Form a group of friends and share different types of questions along with different methods of solving them. When you will start solving problems by yourself, you will be surprised to see that you want to do many more."

Rahul saw that Sachin was getting more and more interested in learning the techniques of developing subject matter expertise.

So he said, "Finally, let me give you the master card of '16 Whys?'"

Sachin was surprised, as he had never heard this term ever before in his life. He looked at Rahul questioningly.

Rahul clarified, "This is a Japanese way of developing subject matter expertise. And you must know that the Japanese are well known for their detailing and working to develop the best in class products such as cars, electronics. This is developed through asking questions like 'Why? How? What? When? Where?' for every problem faced. Why don't you choose the topic, Sachin, and we will play the game of 'Why?'"

Sachin said, "Electricity in physics?"

"Okay," agreed Rahul. "Let's start. How does electricity get generated?"

Sachin thought for a while, and said, "Due to the flow of electrons in atoms."

"Next, 'How'?"

"When the metal is given external force such as heat or magnetism, this force increases the vibrations of electrons. This vibration loosens the bond of electrons so some start moving freely. Their flow is responsible for the phenomenon of electricity in the metal."

"How do you generate proper electricity to light a bulb?"

"When you connect a charged battery to two ends of a conductor, the other ends of which are also connected to the light bulb. The potential difference between +ve and −ve ends of the battery acts as the external force as mentioned above, which gives rise to electric current, which is nothing but flow of electrons from the −ve end towards the +ve end. This flow results in the flow of electricity, which is responsible for the ignition of the filament in the bulb, which in turn produces light."

Sachin realized, as he answered each question correctly, that his interest and enthusiasm in pursuing more about physics was increasing. This interest and enthusiasm acted as a catalyst for his search for knowledge. As more questions were asked, there was greater curiosity within him to get to the depth of the subject, to know more. This further helped tease the brain for known information, giving it a definite shape and understanding. And for the answers which were unknown, there was an identified need for finding the right and appropriate answers, from appropriate sources. Sachin understood that this session with Rahul had set him on the pursuit of knowledge and learning.

Sachin was convinced at the end of the discussion that there was nothing like good memory or bad memory. The ability to remember a subject or topic is directly linked to a genuine liking for that subject, which can be developed with some effort. In order to develop expertise in weak subjects, he realized, he needed to get into details and understand each topic thoroughly, ask questions and practice more.

After consistent efforts, he would reach such a stage of mental acceptance that eventually he would enjoy everything about that particular subject.

*　　*　　*

Three months had passed since the challenge had been launched between the two teams of Bhattacharya and Rahul. It was 10am, on Saturday. Rahul was busy taking mathematics with his batch of thirty students. He was teaching them fractions that day.

"Okay, who will explain to me the concept of fraction of a number?"

Around 15 hands went up promptly.

Rahul looked at them all and said laughingly, "You guys are picking up. Okay, Shankar you explain."

"Sir, suppose, we six friends go for a movie. After watching the movie, we feel hungry so we go to a restaurant to eat pizza. We order two pizzas, one for this hefty Ameya who will eat a full pizza by himself… so there is no fraction. But the rest of us will eat 5 slices of the second pizza, so we will have to make 5 equal parts of one pizza. We have a total of 5 slices of pizza. Now I feel hungrier, so I take 2 parts, so I get 2 out of 5; Gautam and the rest take one part each, so he gets 1 out of 5. In this way, fraction helps us distribute each number or thing evenly."

Rahul said, "Great, Shankar. I am very happy to note that you are picking up so well. What's the reason for such brilliance?"

Madhuri noticed that Shankar's face glowed at this praise and appreciation; his joy brought a smile on her face. Rahul next turned his attention on Gautam.

"Gautam Dada, can you convert Shankar's and others' fractions into percentage?"

Gautam got up from his seat but could not explain.

As Rahul was talking to Gautam, Ameya stood up, practically jumping eagerly, saying, "Sir, should I tell you? I know the answer."

Rahul looked at him and said, "It's good, Ameya, that you know the answer. I will ask you the next question but this one is for Gautam, so he will answer."

Ameya sat down.

Rahul turned his attention back to Gautam and smiled at him.

"Not sure? Let's look at it again…" and he turned towards the blackboard and started writing down. "What is percentage?"

"Sir, it means part of 100."

"Absolutely correct!"

"Now, what do you do in case you want to take the percentage of something? You take the denominator of a fraction and try to convert it to 100, right?" Rahul asked Gautam.

"So, when Shankar has eaten 2 pieces out of a total of 5, you will write in fraction form as 2/5. Right?"

Gautam replied in the positive.

"Now, if I want to make the base as 100, what shall I do?"

"You will multiply 5 with 20 to get 100," replied Gautam.

"Excellent."

Rahul again turned to the board and multiplied the base of fraction with 20 and wrote 100 in front.

"Now what should I do with the numerator?"

Gautam replied in a hurry, "Sir, multiply it also with 20, so you will get 20/100, so the answer would be 20%."

Rahul exclaimed with joy, "Absolutely. You have done it. Now can you do it for the portions of pizza for the others and tell us who took what percentage of a pizza?"

Gautam moved confidently towards the board to solve the problem given by Rahul Sir. Madhuri felt the mood of the whole class was improving with every session. For the first time since the challenge had started, she felt some hope that Rahul could prove his point to the school management. And if he is proved right, why only her school, the fate of all students across the globe could change!

At the same time, another class was going on in the school premises – Bhattacharya's. Tall and lean Bhattacharya was wearing a white shirt and black trousers that day. He had a long nose, so his face with his glasses perched on it, and penetrating eyes from behind the glasses looked as if a vulture was looking at its prey. It was pure coincidence that he too was teaching the subject of fractions and percentage to students of his batch.

He was addressing the students, "So today we have learnt the chapter of fractions and percentage. How did you like it?"

All the students replied in one voice, "Good, sir."

"That's better. You see, you are all bright students so I do not think that I need to teach you the basics of mathematics. Let us do some tests which will help you in your exams."

He looked at Shivani and asked her, "Can you explain the concept of fraction?"

Shivani Ghosh, first ranker in Section A, had been securing the first position since the last five years in the class.

She got up from her seat and started, "Sir, suppose I went to see a movie with my friends–"

Even before Shivani could proceed with her explanation, Bhattacharya interrupted her, "What, Shivani, why are you bringing a movie in the chapter of fraction? Can you not be direct and explain the concept? Have you not understood? Then you should have asked me."

Shivani wanted to say something but she chose to remain silent; perhaps she did not wish to be put down in front of the whole class again. She told herself, 'sir, I know the concept very well, I simply took an example of a movie to make it simple for everyone in the class and have some fun while learning.' But she dared not speak aloud. She continued to stand.

Bhattacharya turned at Parth Ahuja, another scholar in the class.

"Parth, can you explain the concept? But be brief and don't reach a movie theatre to explain the concept," he said unpleasantly, giving Shivani a sidelong glance; the girl felt even more embarrassed and nervous.

Parth explained, "Sir, a fraction is part of a whole sum, be it any item or a number. For example, if we divide an apple in four parts, each part is the fraction of the full apple."

Bhattacharya was very pleased with the answer, "This is it, Shivani. Learn from Parth."

Parth looked at Shivani and rubbed his forefinger just below his nose as if he was flattening his moustache. Shivani's eyes turned teary, and she blinked hard, just about succeeding in preventing the tears from flowing out, and down her cheeks.

Bhattacharya noticed it but did not bother to calm her down. He looked at Shivani and asked her to sit down.

In a rude, loud tone, he addressed the class, "None of you are aware of what I have put at stake by getting into this competition with that novice and principled Rahul Saxena. You guys can't afford to mess up. You are all very bright and talented, and there is no comparison. That's the reason why I have chosen you all in my team. I have put faith in your capabilities, now it's your turn. You can't fail me, right? And I don't like to fail, under any circumstances and at any cost," and walked out of the class.

As soon as Bhattacharya left, Shivani broke down completely. All her friends like Pratik, Aditi and Santrupt surrounded her to cheer her up.

Pratik said, "*Arrey*, why are you crying? We all know Bhattacharya Sir is short-tempered. What if you could not answer one question of his?"

Shivani stopped crying, looked up, teary faced and said, "No, I knew the answer, I just thought of an example to explain it better, but Sir just doesn't have patience, he stopped me so abruptly. Frankly speaking, in the last three months, he has become so very demanding and difficult that my whole confidence is shaken."

Letting out a deep sigh, she murmured, "I don't know if I'll be able to maintain my rank this year."

The Influence of Company

SIX MONTHS PASSED smoothly since the competition was announced. Rahul had noticed that the students had started enjoying their subjects. Most of the time, they were engrossed in discussions on the topics they had learnt in class, and were trying to improvise on their learning. His efforts had started making a difference in their aptitude, which he thought was a big differentiator.

It was another Sunday morning. As per the weekly schedule, all students and parents had gathered in the school ground to carry out their exercise routine. Everyone was busy, when suddenly there was a noise from one corner of the ground.

Shantabai, Shankar's mother, was talking to a lean man, who was walking towards Rahul.

"Don't go near Sir. Please go away from here. I'm taking care of Shankar, you don't need to bother," she kept repeating to the man.

But ignoring her completely, the man walked briskly towards Rahul, in a hurry to get to him, as quickly as possible.

Realizing that the man would not listen to her pleas, Shantabai grew worried for Rahul, and so she started shouting, "Rahul Sir! Rahul Sir!"

On hearing his name shouted aloud, Rahul looked in that direction. He noticed Shantabai running behind a lean man, who was striding towards him.

By the time Rahul could react, the man had reached Rahul. He greeted Rahul with folded hands, "Namaskar, sir."

"Namaskar," replied Rahul softly, unsure of who that man was and what were his intentions.

His hands still folded and with a pleading look on his face, the man started speaking to Rahul, "Sir, I'm guilty of troubling you and this ma'am," looking at Madhuri, he completed his sentence. He continued, "Not only to you two, I'm also guilty to my wife and own son, whose life I have been playing with till now. It is you, who moved them out of the filth I had put them in! I realize now that it was my biggest mistake to overlook my son's career for the lure of a few free drinks. I beg forgiveness for my deeds, and request you to give me one chance to change the life of my family and people around me."

As he finished speaking, Shantabai came closer to them and said, "Sir, he is my husband and Shankar's father, Tukaram."

Her eyes were moist as she was speaking to Rahul. Tukaram's hands were still folded, regret writ large on his face.

He looked at Shantabai and asked, "Where is Shankar, *maza bala* (my child)?"

He looked so anxious to find his son that he did not even wait for her reply.

His eyes started looking for Shankar, who was standing about 15 feet away. On seeing his son, Tukaram ran towards him and held both his hands in his own. He raised Shankar's left hand and kissed it. Then he gently drew Shankar to him, and hugged him tightly. Poor Shankar didn't know how to react, so he looked at Tukaram and gave him a weak smile.

"How are you, Father?"

Hearing Shankar's voice, Tukaram started crying loudly, "Oh, my son. You are so good. Despite all the troubles I have caused, you are still asking me how I am!" he still held Shankar in his arms.

Shantabai moved closer to Tukaram and said, "Now please stop crying. Both Shankar and I have forgiven you."

Allowing Shankar to move out of his embrace, Tukaram walked to where Rahul was standing, watching this little family scene. Seeing Tukaram wiping his eyes with his palms, Shankar went up to his father and offered his kerchief. At this gesture, Tukaram again broke down.

"How nice of you, Shankar, despite all the troubles I gave you two, you are still so caring."

Tears flowing down his cheeks, Tukaram addressed Rahul, "Sir, I am thankful to you for taking care of my son and working for his education so that he can have a bright future."

Rahul remained silent.

But Madhuri was furious at this drama, so she came forward and charged him, "After creating so much havoc, now you have realized you have a wife and a son? Are you even aware of what sort of slavery you had put your son into while negotiating Shankar's freedom with Dagdu Dada? You must be the first father in the history of mankind to compromise the safety and future of your own son for a glass of free drink. He abused this freedom and Shankar would have discontinued his studies, had Rahul Sir not intervened and freed him from the clutches of Dagdu."

She paused for breath, and continued, "Now that your son is on the path of progress and he has left his terrible past behind, why have you come to him? Why are you disturbing their lives?"

As Madhuri stopped, Shantabai added, "Go back. We don't need you. You go back to your drinking bar and spend your whole life there! We will manage our ways. I am alive for Shankar... to take care of his needs and education."

Hearing this Tukaram turned towards Rahul and pleaded, "Sir, I am here to apologize to everyone, to my own family, you and Teacher Ma'am."

With folded hands he faced Madhuri and said, "I know I have caused a lot of trouble for Shankar and his mother by snatching away the money for Shankar's milk and books to buy bottles of alcohol for myself. She would work the whole month to earn ₹2,000-3,000 and I would snatch away half of it to splurge on useless activities like drinks and gambling. When the money would get exhausted, I would demand more and if she couldn't give me, I would beat her ruthlessly in a fit of rage. My sins cannot be forgotten, but give me one chance to improve and I promise, I will not disappoint you."

His confession and pleas shook everyone on the ground, all of them stopped what they were doing and watched the happenings attentively.

Rahul slowly moved towards Tukaram and held his folded hands.

He said, "I'm happy that you have realized the damage you have done to not only yourself, but your entire family. Your vices almost ruined Shankar's life. Thank God that his haplessness came to my notice and I was able to move him out of that filth created by you and that don."

Rahul continued, looking at the groups of parents and students, "I fail to understand the psychology of people like Tukaram who are hell-bent on ruining not only their own life but that of people around them, that it becomes almost impossible to bring them back to the path of normality and progress. Under the influence of their addiction, they can compromise with anything and everything."

Then looking at Tukaram, he pointed at Shantabai and continued severely, "Look at this humble lady. Despite all the bad things you have done to her, she is still supporting you and your family, working as a domestic help to make two ends meet. Do you know, you have robbed her of her youth, motherhood and totally shattered her confidence and self-respect?"

Tukaram said, "Sir, you are like God for our family. You have not only saved Shankar, but also made me realize my mistakes. That is the reason why I have come here today to seek your support and guidance so that I can reassemble my fractured life. After I separated from Shankar, I realized that I love him. And the strength of my love for Shankar and Shanta are much stronger than my craving for the daily quota of liquor. It is not going to be easy for me to give up liquor, physically and mentally, but I have resolved to give up this bad habit. Can you please help me, because however hard I try to give it up, my thirst for liquor becomes more dominating and it catches me in its demon-like clutches?" he made a very funny face as if this habit was a person and holding him tightly.

Seeing his expression and hearing his argument, Rahul and the whole group started chuckling.

Rahul asked him, "Tell me, are you very sure that you want to give up this habit?"

Tukaram gestured at Shankar and said, "He is the apple of my eyes, I swear on him, and promise to give up liquor but, seriously, I do not know how to do that," he looked totally confused and helpless.

Rahul nodded, "Okay, bring a photograph of Shankar and Shantabai, and meet me here, tomorrow morning, and I will show you the way."

"Sir, I will come tomorrow morning at 8.30am. With the photographs."

After some time, the whole group left the school ground.

Next day, Rahul reached the school ground, at the appointed time and waited for Tukaram, but couldn't see him anywhere. He waited for some time for Tukaram but in vain. Thinking that Tukaram was, in all likelihood, one of those several drunkards, who are big on talk but small on action, he concluded that Tukaram wouldn't come. Rahul sat on a bench and started reading the paper.

As he was engrossed reading the paper, someone greeted him, "Namaskar, sir."

Rahul was surprised to see Tukaram waiting for him. Rahul noticed a complete transformation in his overall appearance. He was looking clean and tidy, with washed black trouser and white half-sleeve shirt. He had shaved off his beard and trimmed his hair. He was looking much better than the previous day.

"Namaskar, Tukaram. How are you?"

"*Bas theek hoon* (I am fine)."

Rahul asked him to sit down, gesturing at the other end of the bench, on which he was sitting.

Rahul kept the newspaper aside, and looked at Tukaram, "Tell me, what's your problem?"

Tukaram was taken aback, "No problem, sir."

"Then why do you drink so much alcohol, to the extent that you have to compromise your routine life, your son's career, your wife's dignity and your own health?"

Tukaram exhaled and said, "It's become an addiction, sir. If I don't drink, I will not be comfortable. That discomfort is so acute that I must have a glass or two of alcohol. Then once I have started drinking, there is no limit. The bartender keeps on pushing for more, so I keep on drinking more."

"How much does a glass of liquor cost?"

"₹50 per glass."

"How many glasses do you have a day?"

"Minimum 3-4 per day, I don't drink that much."

Now Rahul lost his temper. He loudly banged on the bench and, raising his voice, accused him, "You're spending around ₹200-300 a day, that's around ₹6,000-7,000 per month, and still you say you don't drink that much? Do you know how much your wife earns per month, after 6-7 hours of hard work, as a maid at three or four houses?"

Tukaram did not know, it appeared from his body language.

"...₹12,000–15,000 a month and you are saying you spend half of her earning in your liquor. Too bad, too selfish, Tukaram! How can you be so very selfish? Just imagine what must be happening to your wife's sentiments when she sees you peeing off her hard earnings in this way."

Tukaram said in a very soft voice, "I've realized that, and that's why I seek your help to get rid of this bad habit."

Rahul retorted, "I'm not a doctor, so I can't prescribe any

medicine for this. But in my opinion, your problem is more psychological than physical, so I can give you a solution. But it is not easy. Would you be able to follow it?"

"Yes, certainly, with all honesty, I will follow your guidelines."

"Okay, then listen to me carefully. You will carry in your pocket, photographs of your son and wife. Whenever you have an urge to drink, you will take it out, look at it and say, 'if I drink liquor, I will be breaking my promise of your well-being. I will not take the drink'. Saying this, you will spot jog till 100. With this mental exercise, your craving will be checked, in all probability. If you still want to drink, you will punch a hole on their photos. The number of holes on their photos will remind you of the number of times you have broken your promise. I am sure if your conscious mind is alert, and your love for your family is deep, you will not have more than four or five holes on the photographs," Rahul paused, and looked at Tukaram.

Tukaram said, "Sir, I promise you that I won't disappoint anyone in this challenge. I am not as learned as you are, but like you, I'm also father and if you can give up a bright career and tonnes of money for your son's well-being, I just have to give up my bad habit. I will give up, sir, I promise I will give up," saying this, he got up from the bench and walked towards the school gates, leaving behind an astonished Rahul.

At around 9pm that night, there was a knock on Tukaram's door, in Rajiv Gandhi Nagar. Shantabai was washing utensils post-dinner, while Tukaram was sitting on a chair and watching Shankar who was studying. Shankar was sitting on the floor, an overturned kitchen utensil serving as his study table.

On hearing the knock, Shankar got up and opened the door. It was Sukhdev, an old-time friend of Tukaram's, and his companion for evening parties; it seemed he had come to call him for that evening's session. Hesitantly, he asked if Tukaram was in; seeing him, Shantabai made a face of intense dislike and Shankar got nervous. Tukaram got up from the chair and moved out of the room.

There was silence in the room and outside, which did not last long. Suddenly, there was a noise outside, of two people quarrelling. Curious, Shantabai opened the door to see what was happening. Shankar too was curious and wanted to check what the noise was about, but Shantabai asked him to stay inside and continue studying. Shantabai heard Tukaram refusing to join Sukhdev, and a disappointed Sukhdev trying to convince him.

"Tukaram, my dear friend, you and I are old friends. We have been together for so long, how can you deny giving me company? I understand you don't want to drink, don't drink, but at least sit with me. Come and sit there."

Hearing this, Shantabai lost her temper, and shouted at him, "You widower! You have any self-respect or not? After great difficulty, Tukaram has decided to give up alcohol and lead a peaceful life for his own sake and our family, and you are hell-bent on spoiling it? You scoundrel! Are you leaving this place on your own or should I help you with my broom?"

Seeing her mood, Sukhdev slunk off, sullenly.

Late that night, Tukaram woke up from his sleep. His whole body was twitching, as if his muscles were being pulled in two opposite directions. His mouth felt dry. He wanted to get up, but it wasn't easy. He tried to shout and call Shantabai but despite tremendous effort, not even a squeak came out of him! He wiped his face; it was full of sweat. He felt a very strong urge for a glass of liquor. He got up from his bed, and realized his walk was not straight; he was tripping and unstable. He told himself, 'what I need is a glass of liquor and that too only for today. From tomorrow, I will have the strength to give up drinking totally, but today if I don't have it, I may die.' His mind was arguing with itself to convince him for one glass of drink. 'That's the best decision, let me have one glass today, I will gain strength so from tomorrow onwards, I don't need to have even one glass.' He wore his slippers, opened the door and headed to his daily joint.

As he sat at the table, he realized he was totally exhausted. 'This has never happened earlier,' he told himself, 'why is it that I'm feeling so very tired? So heavy?'

Seeing him, the bar owner strolled over to him, and welcomed him.

"Well, well, Tukaram! Sukhya was saying you have given up liquor? Why? You don't have money? Pay me next time… when have I asked you for money? So, should I get you your regular and favourite Santara (name of country liquor) glass with snacks?"

Even as the bar owner was speaking, Tukaram was in a different world, struggling with his own self. Soon a bar boy brought him a bottle and an empty glass.

"Ice?" asked the boy.

Tukaram stared back, blankly. The boy put some ice in the glass and poured out the liquor. He went back and returned with a plate of snacks.

The bar owner who was still standing near Tukaram, said, "You may start now. Your favourite drink is ready. Enjoy!"

Satisfied that he hadn't lost a regular customer, the owner returned to his desk.

Tukaram sat staring at the table, on which stood a glass of his favourite drink and a plate of snacks.

"One sip and all problems will vanish," said a voice from somewhere deep inside.

He stretched out his right hand towards the glass and grasped it firmly. Looking at the glass filled with liquor, his eyes sparkled, and a smile hovered on his face. He moved his hand towards his mouth, but suddenly he saw Shankar's face. He then remembered what Rahul Sir had told him that morning and the promise he had made to Rahul. Setting the glass down on the table, Tukaram took out his wallet, where he had kept his wife's and son's photographs. He gazed at these and, unknowingly, he reached for the glass and picked it up.

In his mind's eye, Tukaram drifted to the past, and saw an eight-month-old toddler trying to get up and walk. Try as he might, the little fellow couldn't stand up by himself; he would try to stand up, but would fall down, midway.

As Tukaram went back to those days in the past, he murmured to himself, "Those days were filled with lots of hope and little despair, plenty of smiles and small regrets, but overall it was a great time."

Finally, the boy managed to get up, and swaying unsteadily, started walking towards his parents, who were very excited to witness his first successful attempt at walking. The boy was walking towards Tukaram, who was thrilled, and wanted to take the baby in his arms, hug him, and shower his love on his child! But, wait, what is this? Before the toddler could come close to those outstretched arms, he fell down, and started wailing! Perhaps he had got hurt or was disappointed or both. As time passed, his screams grew louder and louder. Suddenly, Tukaram saw toddler Shankar turning into a teenaged boy crying his heart out, with the same hurt, sadness and disappointment.

'Seeing' this, the horrified Tukaram started shivering, and he couldn't hold the glass any longer. He knew not why, but all of a sudden, he hurled the glass on the floor, kicked the table with such force that it toppled over, and with it fell the bottle, which contained the rest of the liquor, and the plate of snacks. Hearing the noise, all those sitting in the bar looked at Tukaram. The bar owner came running up to Tukaram, wondering at the commotion. Tukaram still sat on his chair, dazed.

"What happened?" then, seeing the table, plates, and bottle on the floor, bellowed, "Oh my God! What a mess? Why did you do this?"

He was furious with Tukaram, pounced on him, grabbed his collar, shook him hard and viciously slapped Tukaram. Weak Tukaram collapsed.

Kicking Tukaram continuously, the owner growled, "I served you, and you have thrown it all away, you!"

But in spite of it all, there was a slight smile on Tukaram's face. He was murmuring to himself, "Shankar, see I have not taken a drink today. After so many years, I will pass tonight without a glass of drink. This is for you, my son, this is for you."

The bar owner continued to kick him, and with no one to protect Tukaram, the frail man slipped into deep sleep, perhaps even unconsciousness.

★   ★   ★

Rahul woke up as the alarm went off. It was 5.30am. After freshening up, he left for the park. Today, he had worn a black track suit with white-coloured jogging shoes.

After a few minutes, he was in the park and started jogging. It was then that he saw Tukaram standing at one corner of the park, about 15 feet away. There was a wound on his face, blood clots on his forehead. Grains of sand and grass stuck on the bloodied wounds. Blood had dried, so it was obvious to Rahul that Tukaram had not got any first aid done on his wounds. It seemed as if someone might have hit him on his forehead, causing the injury.

Looking at Tukaram, Rahul was shaken from inside. Tukaram looked at him, folded his hands and greeted him politely.

"Namaskar, sir."

"What happened? How did you get hurt? Did someone hit you last night?"

Smiling, Tukaram moved closer and said, "Sir, I've come to show you something."

Rahul got anxious at Tukaram's condition, so he didn't pay much attention to what he said about showing him something.

He questioned the man again, "You can tell me that later, but first I want to know what happened to you last night."

But Tukaram was in a different mood altogether, and didn't reply to Rahul's specific query. He pulled out two photographs from his pocket and said, "See, there are no punch marks on these photos," his voice trembled as he said this, his eyes turning moist. "Sir, last night I didn't drink any alcohol. I'm feeling extremely happy and proud today, I just can't describe it in words."

Now it was time for Rahul to feel happy. Rahul was very pleased with this statement.

He forgot his query on Tukaram's condition, and patted his back and said, "Good, Tukaram, for the first time after so many years, you have given preference to your family over your addiction. And how people have taken your choice is visible on your face, in the form of blood stains and wounds. But at least

225

you could have cleaned your wound; else you may catch an infection."

Tukaram said cheerfully, "Sir, now nothing can happen to me. I have overpowered my biggest enemy, alcohol. This is a small thing in comparison."

Rahul took Tukaram to his house and cleaned his wounds, dabbed a disinfectant on it, bandaged his wound and offered him a cup of tea with some biscuits.

As Tukaram was leaving for his home, Rahul warned him, "It's good you did not drink liquor for one day, but you will also have to prepare yourself for more struggles in your life – and not only that, be ready to support Shankar in his struggle."

"But I'm totally dumb, illiterate... what support can I give him?"

"Don't think small of your contribution, do what you can to help Shankar. Your emotional support can do wonders, Tukaram," Rahul paused and advised, "give him the confidence that he is not alone in his struggle. Parents who are not adequately educated can give emotional support to their kids. This emotional support can give unbeatable confidence to kids."

Tukaram looked at Rahul with gratitude, and left for his home.

Start of a Countdown

IT WAS MONDAY, 8.30am. As Rahul entered his class, the office boy came in and gave him a chit. It was from Principal Sir, informing him that the education ministry was taking deep interest in the ongoing competition and would be deputing a team of experts to meet the concerned teachers and participating to judge how the two theories were developing.

In the chit, the principal expressed his intention to arrange a meeting of the visiting delegates with Rahul's batch students. Rahul understood, though it was not mentioned explicitly, that the intention of Principal Daruwala and the education ministry could be to check the progress made by his batch in the competition. After reading the chit, Rahul looked at his batch students, who were busy doing their work.

"Hello, children! Pay attention here, please. There is good news. You all have a great opportunity to demonstrate your knowledge, skills and learning so far to a group of distinguished guests and our own Principal Sir who have expressed their willingness to pay a visit to our class and check your progress."

There was a loud uproar of enthusiasm and excitement among the batch mates. As the noise subsided, Rahul continued, "Can I invite them tomorrow evening?"

"Anytime, sir! It will be fun to be with them," the students chorused cheerfully.

Rahul wrote '4pm' on the chit and returned it to the office boy.

After some time, the office boy knocked on the door of a room where Bhattacharya was teaching his class. Bhattacharya was busy scolding one of the students, Shivani Ghosh.

"How many times do I have to teach you the same subject? You are just not catching up."

Shivani tried to explain, "But sir–"

"What 'but sir'?" he interrupted her and continued severely, "Shivani, I selected you in my batch because you are a rank-holder. You should set an example for others to follow, but sadly now you are not able to come up to your own performance standard. You are failing, Shivani, do you know you are failing? I have done so much for you, now you must perform."

Speaking to Shivani, his voice had become loud enough to send a shiver down the spine of the office boy, who was waiting for a chance to speak.

Bhattacharya turned back, looked at the office boy and bellowed at him, "Yes? What can I do for you?"

The office boy fumbled, could not find words for some time. But a few moments later, having mustered courage, he said, "Principal Sir has sent this message for you."

He handed the chit to Bhattacharya. The teacher opened it and read it. 'Oh my God! Delegates from the education ministry and Principal Sir want to meet the class and see how far the students have progressed since the competition started. I'm not sure, but the current performance of my batch students will be my downfall,' Bhattacharya thought. Then he looked at the calendar and wrote down a date, of meeting them a week later. The office boy took the chit and went away.

Bhattacharya turned back to the students and announced, "Now see, you have it. The education ministry is taking deep interest in this competition. They are deputing a delegation to meet all of you. I have suggested a date, a week from today. I suggest all of you prepare well for this meeting. I hope you will not disappoint me and Principal Sir, and spoil my reputation in front of them."

In the evening as Bhattacharya was leaving school, the office boy met him in the corridor and informed him, "Principal Sir has asked you to meet him before you leave for home."

"But I gave him a time in the afternoon, then why does he want to meet me? Do you know?" he scowled at the office boy.

"No, sir," replied the boy, and left the place.

Bhattacharya started for the principal's office.

After some time, Bhattacharya was sitting with the principal in his room.

The principal said, "You mentioned next week, but the education ministry has some delegates coming from abroad, so I've received a message from the education minister, Sushilkumar Joshi's PA, that they are coming tomorrow to our school. I'm sorry, I won't be able to accept your suggested time, however, I can offer you a little flexibility to choose your time slot: either at 3pm or at 5pm, because they are meeting Rahul's team at 4pm. Your team can meet them before or after they have met Rahul's team."

Bhattacharya pondered at this information. 'Oh, they are meeting Rahulbaba's team too. That would be interesting... to watch those duffers failing to impress delegates and spoil Rahul's reputation forever. Rahul will not be able to show his face to anyone in school, and who knows he may even leave school forever?' At the thought of Rahul leaving the school in failure and shame, a smile appeared on his face.

As he was in deep thought, he didn't catch what the principal had said for the next few minutes.

"Hey Bhattacharya, give me a time... 3pm or 5pm? I have to confirm to the PA."

With a lot of hesitation, Bhattacharya replied, "But, sir. We are not yet prepared."

"Don't worry, this is not the final exam. They just want to see the progress made by your batch so far. They will be meeting Rahul's batch students too."

Hearing Rahul's name Bhattacharya was quick to quip, "That would be nice, sir. Rahulbaba and his students will get some moral boost."

It seemed as though the principal did not like such comments, so he reacted immediately, speaking sharply, "You need not worry about Rahul and his batch students. You tell me the time."

"Three, sir. Though there is no time left for preparation, still we will manage."

Principal Daruwala leaned towards the intercom, pressed the button on the phone and said, "Anjali, please fix the time from 2.30pm to 5pm, for the delegates."

Bhattacharya came out of the principal's room, preoccupied.

"So, tomorrow is an important day to win the battle against Rahulbaba. I have made a smart choice of selecting bright students who will surely perform better than students in Rahul's batch. In a way, I will win the first half of the competition tomorrow itself. This win will take away all hope and confidence of the other party. They will neither have any interest nor the confidence to work for the rest of the competition," Bhattacharya muttered to himself gleefully. "Rahul's theory will fail, yes, it must fail. After all, he has dared to challenge my style of teaching, which I have mastered over all these years." A strange smile appeared on his face.

Slowly, news started spreading that, the education ministry was taking deep interest in the competition between the batches of Bhattacharya and Rahul Saxena. And with the news that, delegates from the education ministry were to meet batch students of both the groups, excitement reached its peak!

★   ★   ★

Madhuri had prepared herself well that day; after all, it was the most important day in her life, as students of Rahul's batch were to appear for the test. In other words, it was Rahul's theory that would be tested. She felt it was not Rahul's test but the test of her belief in Rahul, his personality, intelligence, thoughts, his kindness and sensitivity towards everyone around. Add to this, the sharpness with which he could read the other's thoughts yet display such humility that he never let the other person feel inferior but always used these skills to support people around him.

Her thoughts drifted to Rahul. He was like a magnet, which attracted even the tiniest iron particle to it. Indeed, Rahul's presence gave confidence to people around him. Her thoughts started revolving around the effect that Rahul had on her. There

231

was a bright smile on her face, which had turned pinkish as she thought of Rahul. Suddenly, she became conscious of her thoughts and tried to hide her feelings, hoping that no one had seen her blushing.

But was it possible to hide the sparkle of her smile on that beautiful pinkish face from the sun, who was observing her from the distance? And as he saw her smile, he moved out from behind the clouds to the clear sky so that he could see her more clearly. Had the sun become brighter, or was that the effect of love?

★   ★   ★

At around 9.30am, the security officer positioned at the main gate called up Anjali.

"Ma'am, reporters of World News are at the gate. They want to meet Principal Sir and take his interview. Should I allow them?"

Anjali was surprised, "Who could have called them? I have not. Neither would Principal Sir because generally I handle such tasks."

She asked the security officer to hand over the phone to the concerned newsperson.

After a little pause, someone spoke on the other end of the line, "Good morning, ma'am. My name is Aniruddha Mehta from World News. We would like to meet Principal Daruwala and take his interview. If possible, we would also like to have a live coverage of the competition going on in your school," he paused for some time and then added, "we have information that a famous technocrat, Rahul Saxena, has got into some unique competition with an experienced and veteran teacher in your school about teaching methodologies. Since both children and

232

studies are of interest to all parents and families, we wish to cover the competition to the best extent possible."

Without checking with Principal Sir, Anjali was not in a position to give permission, so she said, "Mr Mehta, I have to check with Principal Sir if we can give you permission for his interview and the live coverage. Please give me some time. I will check and get back to you," and disconnected.

She rushed to the principal's room, but he wasn't there. Even his mobile was lying on his desk. Anjali was at a fix as she realized that he had probably gone to visit the classes. 'What should I do,' she wondered, feeling helpless.

As she was thinking, she saw Bhattacharya in the corridor. He was coming towards the principal's room. Being a senior member of the teaching staff, Anjali thought that perhaps Bhattacharya could guide her. She greeted him when he came closer.

"Good morning, sir."

"Good morning, Anjali. How are you?"

"I am fine, sir. I need a small help from you."

"Yes, yes tell me. What can I do?"

She narrated to him the call from the security officer at the gate and request from reporters of World News that they would like to interview Principal Sir and also take a live coverage of the delegates' visit from the education ministry.

Bhattacharya was delighted to hear this. 'This is a God-given opportunity! Now the whole world will know about my success. What a great chance,' he thought.

Looking at Anjali, he asked coolly, "So what's the issue? It's good to know that they are taking an interest in the activities of our school."

"That's true, but I don't know where to find Principal Sir as he is on his rounds, visiting classes. I'm not sure whether we should allow them or not. What should I do?"

With a mysterious smile on his face, Bhattacharya asked convincingly, "Why should we not allow them? Do you think Principal Sir would not like the publicity of our school and this project? I think he would approve such publicity. You must allow them."

Unable to contact Principal Daruwala and totally confused, Anjali seemed to get her answer after talking to Bhattacharya, so she went back to her desk, picked up the phone and told Security to allow the media inside the school premises. As vans of news agencies entered the premises, the school became the news centre, because as news of World News entering the grounds spread, other news channels too started appearing at the main gate.

Within the next one hour, TV channels across the country were buzzing with breaking news of the competition involving the two competing theories of imparting knowledge and learning between the teams of Rahul and Bhattacharya.

Rahul was teaching his batch students, when the office boy came running into the class.

"Sir, there is a call on your mobile."

Rahul did not carry his mobile into the class, because of two reasons. First, the school's policy did not allow students to carry or use mobiles in school premises, so he believed in leading by setting an example – what is disallowed for students should hold true for teachers as well, in order to create a positive impression of the restriction. Second, the mobile would interfere with his teaching. So he would leave his mobile in his staffroom with the office assistant. This was the first time that the office boy had brought his mobile to his class. He looked at the office boy with displeasure.

The office boy understood and apologized, "Sir, sorry to disturb you. I know you don't like calls when you are teaching, but this is urgent."

Rahul took the mobile.

"Hello! This is Rahul Saxena speaking."

"Hello, Rahul."

Rahul recognized the person on the other side. It was Sunil Parekh, his close friend.

"Rahul, what's going on in your school, *yaar*?"

Rahul was surprised, "What's going on, Sunil? What are you talking about?"

"About this breaking news on TV, almost all channels are covering the competition between you and Bhattacharya in your school. They are also saying that the education ministry is taking a deep interest in this competition."

"Okay, let me check," Rahul said, and disconnected the call.

He was extremely surprised. 'What's going on,' he thought. 'How come news channels have entered the school premises, and who is feeding them information about the competition, the sole purpose of which is the well-being of the students. By prematurely announcing the competition to the world, the batch students would be under tremendous pressure to excel, which is not advisable.'

He decided to talk to Principal Daruwala immediately and request him to stop the news transmission. He dialled the principal's number, but there was no response at the other end.

Giving the children some work that would keep them busy, he went to the principal's office, but he wasn't there. He walked to where Anjali was sitting.

"Where is Principal Sir?" he asked her.

"I don't know, sir. May I help you?"

"Yes, what's this news going about on TV channels? Who allowed them?" Rahul demanded, annoyed.

"I allowed them, Rahulbaba," said a voice from behind him.

It was Bhattacharya. Rahul was taken aback at Bhattacharya's tone. He remained silent.

Bhattacharya continued, "You see, our competition is becoming the talk of the town. Everyone seems to be interested in knowing details of the competition and the obvious outcome."

"Obvious?" Rahul queried, puzzled.

"Rahulbaba, don't mind my saying obvious, but one just needs a bit of common sense to judge which batch will win. Just look at the background of the students of the two batches, it is not difficult to judge which batch will win."

Rahul understood what Bhattacharya was referring to, but he continued to project ignorance.

"It is not obvious to me Bhattacharya Sir, can you please elaborate, what is obvious in the outcome of our competition."

"Don't be so naïve, Rahulbaba, obviously my batch will win. Just look at the students in my batch, they are all toppers, in every exam. Don't mind, but if you compare them with the students of your batch, they are all also scorers but when you count from backwards. Last benchers, you see," Bhattacharya said with a wicked smile on his face.

Rahul started smiling.

"But you selected the students of both the batches, even for my batch!"

He paused for some time and added, "Do you mean to say you made an unfair selection? That you deliberately offered me weak students? Did you have the sole objective of winning the competition from day one? That means you never made an honest attempt to participate in this competition because you yourself were not confident about your theory, and your own teaching method which you have been practising for so many years."

In a very soft but firm voice, Rahul continued to lambast Bhattacharya, "Mr Bhattacharya, I hold you in high esteem, I have always treated you like my elder brother. That's why I put my whole trust in you and asked you to recommend names of students not only for your batch but even for my batch! And you played a game with me?

"Do you know playing a game of one vs other, in other words, politics for personal gains, is our national disease? We, Indians, are excellent individually but when it comes to team spirit, we lose out.

"But don't bother, Mr Bhattacharya, I am not at all worried about the outcome of this competition because I am confident about my belief in the theory that I have proposed and also on the capabilities of the young minds who are at work. And, by the way, I have not adopted any short cut in winning this competition because, for me, more than my success it is the future of the children, of not only my batch, but children all over the world. Their future and career is much more important than my personal gain. I firmly believe that if children adopt even 1 per cent of my proposed theory, they would not only be great students but also great citizens which any country would be proud of!" and Rahul turned to go back to his class.

Principal Daruwala was standing about 6-7ft away, quietly listening to the conversation between Rahul and Bhattacharya. Along with him stood Anjali, Madhuri and Meenakshi. Rahul looked at them and carried on. Slowly, the principal went towards his chamber, Anjali in tow. Madhuri headed to her class and Meenakshi moved closer to Bhattacharya, who was looking down, and seemed to be in deep thought. Meenakshi moved forward, and held his hand and patted it.

After some time, Meenakshi too moved away, without saying a word, removing his hand from Bhattacharya's grip. Stunned, Bhattacharya remained in the corridor.

★ ★ ★

It was around 11am on Tuesday. The school's security guard was amazed by the kind of crowd that had gathered outside the school gates. And to his surprise, the crowd was just getting bigger and bigger with the passage of time. The guard again called up Anjali, seeking her advice. At that time, she was on her way to the school. She in turn, called up Principal Sir, who too was quite shocked at the unexpected public interest in the school.

But one person was extremely happy. Politician Pratap Dikshit. He was happy that on that day, after the delegates from the education ministry would have met students of both the batches, a character named Rahul would be permanently thrown out of the school. His group consisting of Bhattacharya, Meenakshi and some more teachers would regain their diffused power. Once again, he would be at the helm of affairs! His mobile started ringing, distracting his train of thoughts.

"Hello!" said the politician.

"Hello! Bhai, there is good news."

"Yes, I know but I want to hear from you, tell me, what is the good news?"

"Bhai, happy days are here again! After the news channels broadcast the story, people are just gathering outside the school gates since morning. Parents, teachers of other schools, students of other schools and even those who are in no way associated with the school are also gathering outside the school gates to witness the ongoing drama, initiated by that fool Rahul, but smartly played by our great Mr Bhattacharya and Meenakshi Sir."

Pratap replied, "Yes, I know. Keep an eye open and keep me posted about the latest developments from time to time."

He disconnected the phone. A mysteriously naughty smile appeared on his face.

Meantime, in school, at around 11.30am, Bhattacharya was addressing the class.

"Students, you are all aware that the time has come for all of you to prove yourselves and show the world that you are the best. Today, at 3pm, Principal Sir has organized a visit of delegates from the education ministry to our class. They are all distinguished people associated with education and they may have a one-to-one meeting with you. They may judge the success of my teaching through questions asked to you. I have worked very hard to give you all the knowledge and learning that I know, and now it is your turn to give back. I have given you my best, I am sure you will not let me down."

He looked around and asked, "Any questions?"

Shivani raised her hand.

He looked at her and said, "Yes? What do you want to know?"

Hesitantly, Shivani asked, "Sir, what is the objective of their visit to our school and our class in particular? And what if they ask us any question and we can't answer it correctly?"

Irritated, Bhattacharya replied, but without showing his annoyance, "Why would you not know the answer? I have taught you all that there is in the syllabus and what you are supposed to know. After doing all this, it is not acceptable that you don't know the answer. I have done my best, now it is your turn. You can't fail me, is it clear?"

Shivani, true to her outspoken and frank nature, did not stop. She continued to ask questions.

She stood up again, and said, "Sir, are they going to judge our performance in the competition? That means, they will be visiting Rahul Sir's class as well. What if that class does better than us in the performance?"

This last question acted like a bomb to explode Bhattacharya, who was clearly infuriated by now.

He snapped at her, "Your habit of asking unnecessary questions irritates me most of the times. What marks did you get in your exam last year?"

His question to Shivani and his unexpected reaction rattled her, so she remained silent.

"Shivani, why are you silent now? I'm asking you," he practically roared at her. "Tell the whole class, how much did you get in the exam last year?"

"I was first in class, sir."

"Okay, and what was the rank of most of the students in our batch last year? Either first or second rank. True?"

Shivani nodded.

Then he looked at Parth and asked, "Do you know the average marks of most of the students in Rahul's batch?"

Parth, a known supporter of Bhattacharya and his principles, smiled and said, "Nothing much to talk about, sir, most of them are failures. Still, one can say that they all scored first or second rank – but if counted in the reverse order."

As the whole class started laughing, Bhattacharya looked elated.

"Yes, they are no comparison to you all. You are the best and that is what you have to prove again," and looking at Shivani, he added sarcastically, "don't ever doubt yourself."

Shivani had a sinking feeling. She felt like running away from this class and from people like Parth and Bhattacharya, but she was helpless!

In fact, most of the children were getting stressed because of the upcoming meeting with the delegates and the high expectation set by Bhattacharya that they had to be right all the time.

At the same time in some other class, another parallel meeting was going on. Rahul was addressing his class.

"Dear children! Eight months have passed since we all got together and formed a team. I am happy to see the progress made by each one of you. You have all picked up a significant amount of knowledge on each subject, which can take your learning further. More than that, what each one of you has done is to develop the right kind of attitude towards studies. The topic which used to bore you earlier, I'm pleased to see, is generating a good amount of liking, excitement and passion in all of you, which will take you a long way from here."

Rahul paused to look at the students and then continued, "Today is a great day for all of us. As you know, the delegates from the education ministry will be meeting us and enriching our knowledge. They are all distinguished people with very successful careers in the field of education. I'm sure you will have an interesting session with all of them."

Suddenly Shankar raised his hand.

Rahul asked him, "Yes, Shankar, do you have any question?"

"Yes, sir."

Rahul smiled at him and said, "Go ahead."

"Sir, what if they ask us a question and we don't know the answer, what then?"

Rahul looked at him, frowning, "How come? You are so intelligent, why wouldn't you know the answer?"

Shankar started becoming nervous; the feeble smile on his face conveyed his lack of confidence.

Rahul added softly, "Don't worry, if you don't know the answer, they will tell you the right answer."

The entire class erupted with laughter, and the tension dissipated.

★   ★   ★

It was 2.30pm. The principal's office was quite active with teachers, office boys and staff moving in and out of the office preparing to welcome the delegates. The principal himself was supervising the arrangements, advising Anjali on every small detail.

Principal Daruwala continued rattling out instructions to Anjali, "Have you checked everything? As they arrive, they will be received with bouquets, and then they will be seated in the conference room and offered tea and snacks. Next, teachers will be introduced, and the staff, along with the presentation on our school's history, achievements and future plans. After that, they will visit Bhattacharya and Rahul Saxena's classes, and after that…" and so he went on, with Anjali taking down all the points at a furiously fast pace, to keep up with the principal.

After about 10 minutes or so, she received a call from Security, announcing the arrival of the delegates. She informed Principal Daruwala and together they hastened to the entrance of the office building. The entire corridor became active, people moving about with excitement. Some of them wanted to see the delegates, others to complete their given work.

Two white cars arrived in the school portico. Principal Sir and Anjali walked up to the cars to receive the delegates.

Principal Daruwala welcomed them warmly, shook hands with the delegates, and then led them to the conference room near his office. As they settled down, the invited office staff and teachers walked into the conference room and took their seat. Next, tea and snacks were served, over which everyone present participated in the general conversation. Once tea was over, Principal Sir stood up and addressed the gathering formally.

"Good evening, Shri Sushilkumar Joshi, Secretary, Education Ministry; Mrs Padmavati Shetty, Member of Executive Committee, and ex-Principal of Modern School and author of several books on child education and development; Mrs Shailaja Shinde, Commissioner, Education Ministry; and Dr Premshankar Mahajan, Principal Secretary, Govt. of Maharashtra. I am pleased to inform you all that Dr Premshankar has an old association with our school; he did his schooling from this particular school. His son Amit Mahajan also studied here, and now his grandson Ameya Mahajan is a student in our school. It is a matter of great pleasure and honour to receive all of you in our school."

Principal Sir then gave a brief introduction of the school's history and achievements. Next, he introduced the staff and teachers, one by one.

Then Principal Sir introduced the delegates to Rahul.

"This is Rahul Saxena, who has joined our school in the current year. Rahul–"

Before he could proceed further, Sushilkumar Joshi interrupted, smiling warmly at Rahul, "There is no need to introduce Rahul, he is one of India's best technocrats. It is a matter of great pride and honour for us that a man of his calibre has decided to take up education as his career. I am sure he will bring many innovations in the field of education and child development. As a matter of fact, our visit to your school is inspired by some of the novel thoughts he has introduced in your school. We are very keen to meet the students," then looking at the principal he added, "can you give us an idea about the competition between the two groups? It's been the talk of the town now, and most news channels are talking about it."

Principal Daruwala gave a brief about the competition and called Bhattacharya and Rahul up close to them.

After about 15 minutes, Sushilkumar Joshi said, "Let's spend some time with the students."

Everyone rose, and they all walked towards Bhattacharya's class, led by the principal, who conversed with Mr Joshi as they walked along.

As they entered the class, the students stood up, and greeted the group politely, "Good evening, sirs and madams."

"Good evening, students," responded the members of the delegate in a chorus.

Bhattacharya and Principal Sir walked to the back of the class, and sat down on benches, while the delegates sat on chairs kept at the front of the class, facing the children, near the blackboard.

Sushilkumar got up from his seat and addressed the students.

"Dear students, my name is Sushilkumar and we are here to

spend some time with you. If I may express myself, today is a very special day of my life. I am very happy to meet you. We would like to discuss any subject of your choice with you. Which subject would you like to discuss with us?"

Parth got up from his seat and said, "Science, sir."

"Oh great."

Then looking at the other students he asked, "All of you for science?"

"Yes, sir," replied the students in one voice.

"Okay then, what should we discuss in science?" and then after thinking for a few minutes, said, "let's talk about space. That's the hot topic today in India and all over the world."

He started asking questions on space, one after the other, such as...

"What is space?"

Three hands shot up in the class. Shivani, Parth and Pratik Rao raised their hands. Sushilkumar asked Shivani to answer.

She stood up, and answered, "Space consists of things surrounding the earth. Generally, it is referred to things located in the sky, such as planets, stars, the sun, asteroids and other matters located around the surface of the earth."

And then followed other questions...

"What is the planetary constitution of the sun?"

"What is universe?"

"What is a black hole? Why it is called so?"

... And so on... the questions kept on coming and the answers continued. One hour passed, but no one realized it.

Finally Sushilkumar said, "Students, it was great to be with you all. We will have to leave as we have spent more than the allotted time with you. Thank you, and all the best for the future."

The delegation team and the principal moved out of the class. All the students and Bhattacharya looked quite relaxed. 'What will happen to the other class?' Bhattacharya mused, relieved, now that his batch had successfully answered the questions.

Principal Sir led the delegation to Rahul's class. Rahul was waiting outside his class. Seeing Principal Sir and the delegates moving towards his class, he swiftly moved forward and greeted everyone. Led by Rahul and Principal Sir, the delegates entered the class. The students stood up and greeted the members. The delegates returned the greeting and sat on the chairs meant for them, facing the students. Rahul and Principal Sir walked towards the back of the class, and sat down on a bench. Sushilkumar stood up, and addressed the students after introducing himself, and just as he had spoken to the previous group, asked them at the conclusion of the short address, what they would like to discuss.

"Any subject that you may choose, sir," the whole class replied in chorus, cheerfully.

Sushilkumar and all the other delegates were a bit astonished at the confidence of the students.

Sushilkumar thought for some time and said, "Okay, in that case, we will ask you about space. Is it fine with you?"

"Yes, sir," came the reply, loud and clear, leaving Sushilkumar pleasantly surprised.

"What is space?" asked Sushilkumar.

The entire class raised their hands. Sushilkumar had a smile on his face; he looked at the other members of his team, and all of them looked pleased at the response of the students. Sushilkumar looked at the whole class and asked Shankar to respond.

"Sir, I need to understand your question in more detail. Can I seek more clarification about the question itself?"

Sushilkumar was really amazed now. He had not expected such a response.

Nodding his head, he said, "Certainly, please ask your question."

Shankar began politely, "Sir, space has different meanings and context in different branches of studies. For example, in physics, it is often conceived in three-linear dimensions, although modern physicists usually consider it, with time, to be part of a boundless four-dimensional continuum known as space-time. In mathematics, 'spaces' are examined with different numbers of dimensions and with different underlying structures.

"Then again, space has a totally different meaning in astronomy, where it deals with the universe surrounding the earth, covering planetary positions, the sun, stars and other heavenly bodies in the universe. So which space are you referring to, sir?"

For a few moments, Sushilkumar was speechless. Perhaps, he hadn't realized that his question could have such an elaborate answer.

After some time, he asked, "Which space do you want to talk about?"

"Any which you may like to discuss, sir," replied Shankar, confidently.

"Okay, let's talk about physical space; what is that?"

Shankar smiled and proceeded, "In the physical world, space refers to the boundless three-dimensional extent in which objects and events have relative position and direction. Physical space is often conceived in three-linear dimensions, although modern physicists usually consider it, with time, to be part of a boundless four-dimensional continuum known as space-time. The concept of space is considered to be of fundamental importance to an understanding of the physical universe.

"In the seventeenth century, Gottfried Leibniz, the German philosopher-mathematician, and Isaac Newton, the English physicist-mathematician, set out two opposing theories of space. Leibniz held that space is no more than the collection of spatial relations between objects in the world. However, Sir Issac Newton took space to be more than relations between material objects and based his position on observation and experimentation, showing that space must exist independently of matter.

"In 1905, Albert Einstein published a paper on a special theory of relativity, in which he proposed that space and time be combined into a single construct known as space-time. In this theory, the speed of light in a vacuum is the same for all observers – which has the result that two events that appear simultaneous to one particular observer will not be simultaneous to another observer if the observers are moving with respect to one another."

Shankar paused for some time, and was about to resume, but Sushilkumar stopped him. He went near him, put his hand on Shankar's shoulder, and asked, "Where did you get so much of knowledge?"

Shankar looked at Rahul and said, "Sir, taught us all this."

This amazed the delegates further who could not believe that a secondary student could possess so much knowledge on the subject. This interested them, and they posed questions to the students one after another on various subjects. The answers given by all students from Rahul's team overwhelmed them tremendously. It was not only limited to delegates asking the students – they too faced questions from the students who showed a keenness to learn more and more.

Three hours passed and no one realized how time went by! Finally, the delegates moved out of the class.

Sushilkumar looked at Rahul and asked, "Can you join us, please?"

Rahul looked at the principal who nodded his head in affirmation. Rahul accompanied Sushilkumar as they walked down the corridor. Sushilkumar still wasn't out of his hypnotized state; he was full of praise for Shankar and the other students of his class.

He asked, "Is Shankar your student?"

"Yes, he is my student," replied Rahul with a smile on his face.

Sushilkumar said, "In my 35 years of teaching, I have not come across such students, who want to cover a given subject in such great detail! Please accept my congratulations for creating so much passion in the students' mind for going beyond the syllabus."

He paused and asked, "That boy Shankar. He must be a topper in your school, I guess. What is his academic track record so far?"

Rahul became serious and said, "This year he should get good marks."

Sushilkumar looked at him and asked, "No, you have misunderstood my question. I am asking, how has he performed in the past?"

"He failed in his last exams…"

"…And not only the last exam," said a voice from behind them.

It was Principal Sir, who had been listening to their conversation from behind, and well within earshot.

He joined them and continued, "Shankar had a poor track record in studies due to poverty and other circumstances. I came to know much later, that he was also a victim of child abuse by a local don. It was Rahul who fought with all such evil forces and freed him from the clutches of the goon."

While saying this, the principal looked at Rahul with both appreciation and respect.

Principal Sir continued, "I have just recently heard that Rahul was instrumental in freeing Shankar's father from his addiction to alcohol. So, in Rahul, we have a multi-faceted, multi-talented teacher. He is an asset to our school."

He then briefly gave the complete story of how Rahul – under what circumstances – became associated with the school, his revolutionary thoughts on imparting knowledge to students, the resistance put across by senior teachers in the school, the competition between the two groups, allotting students to Rahul, his trust and confidence in his students and their capabilities, and his devotion. He concluded by expressing his delight at the confidence with which the students had interacted with the delegates – a result of all his effort, which they had witnessed some time back in Rahul's class.

By then, they had come out of the school building, and were waiting for the cars to come up to the patio.

Sushilkumar too looked at Rahul with appreciation and said, "Rahul, before I came to your school, I had just heard about you; your background, a very successful career in one of the world's leading companies, your innovations/inventions and now this. I must say, we are proud to have a person of your calibre in our teaching community. Next month, I will be attending a conference in New Delhi, where the country's leading people associated with the teaching community are going to spend three days discussing improved ways of imparting knowledge to the children. The prime minister himself will inaugurate this conference, as he is deeply interested in the upliftment of future generations and improving the capabilities and skills of us citizens. I appreciate your thoughts and methods, so if you permit, I would like to have a word with our respected prime minister about you and your revolutionary methods."

Principal Sir was delighted to hear this. Without waiting for Rahul's answer, he replied on Rahul's behalf, "Yes, please go ahead. If required, we can arrange a seminar which can be conducted by Rahul or alternatively if the PM is interested, I can send him to meet him personally."

"What do you have to say, Rahul?" asked Sushilkumar.

Rahul just smiled at him and remained silent. 'Now, what does the future have in store for me,' he wondered.

I am in Love

THERE WAS NO end to Madhuri's happiness when she learnt how exceptionally well Rahul's students had performed, and the overall comments made by the delegates for Rahul's batch. She was simply not able to express herself.

Sometimes, she felt her happiness had given her wings and she was flying like a fairy; sometimes, she felt completely fulfilled as if she had won the whole world! Sometimes, she felt like the queen of the world and yet again, at times, she felt she was the happiest person in the world! Overall, she felt like laughing, dancing, running… and why not?

Whatever were her feelings for the success of the batch students, one thing was sure: she felt hugely proud of Rahul and his approach for the betterment of the students. One thing also became apparent to her: her sentiments for Rahul. Earlier she had a feeling, but she was unable to put a finger to it, to describe her emotions. Now she knew that she was in love!

In fact, it was only at her second meeting with Rahul on the school ground, that she had started developing a soft spot for him, which had grown gradually into something more – but she hadn't been able to name it. Now, that confusion had gone.

For the first time in her life, Madhuri felt strongly about someone; for the first time, she felt she was so very attracted to someone that she wanted to spend her whole life with him. As she started to think more and more about Rahul, she realized that it might be impossible for her to imagine her life without Rahul!

Today, she had invited Rahul for dinner at her house. Rahul had promised that he would be at her house at 8pm. She looked at the watch… 'oh dear, is it just 6.30pm? Is my watch running slow,' she thought, and then the next moment she laughed at herself for her silly thinking. Though she knew that it was giving the correct time, yet she felt that every moment was unbearably *long*… unending… that time was just not passing. Another first one… for the first time she realized how long and troubling the wait could be for someone, particularly when that someone is your most loved one.

Since Rahul was visiting her house for the first time that day, she herself had made all the preparations for dinner. Now she was arranging the house to make it look sparklingly clean, fragrant and beautiful.

As she took the flower vase, which contained beautifully arranged assorted flowers of rose, orchid and lily, her mind drifted into a different world. A dream world in which she felt she was singing a melody for herself and Rahul!

Somewhere else in the city, Sachin too was in a state of ecstasy. As he came to know about the views expressed by the delegates for their teams' performance, his happiness knew no bounds! For the first time since his return from the hospital, he felt extremely confident. For the first time, he felt he was capable of facing any challenge in life. He thought this was not only his success; it was the success of the whole batch. He called up all his batch mates, one after the other, and informed them about the appreciation showered on their batch by the visiting delegates. All his friends-cum-batch mates decided to meet and celebrate.

253

The Incredible Interview

THE NEWS OF the amazing performance by Rahul's batch spread like wildfire in the city! Almost all news channels and everyone associated with the field of education were discussing only this topic.

People were still not able to believe that a batch of students with an abysmal track record had been able to beat the brightest of students in knowledge and learning!

India's biggest news channel, City News, had arranged for a live talk show on the subject of transformation of the education system. Rahul was invited for an interview by India's leading talk show host, Anjali Ghanekar. The show was scheduled at 9pm the next day.

There was tremendous excitement among those in the teaching fraternity, students, their parents and all those who had even the remotest connection with studies. Even India's large corporate houses had become interested in the news of below-average students growing in knowledge, capability and confidence, and demonstrating it in an incredible Q&A session with some distinguished members of the education ministry.

They all saw a great opportunity in employee-productivity enhancement, which had direct link with a company's profitability.

The next evening, at around 8.45pm, it was as if there was curfew on the roads, with virtually the whole country glued to their TV sets to learn about Rahul Saxena and his path-breaking teaching techniques. Sharp at 9pm, the wait was over and Rahul was seen on the small screen, sitting across Anjali Ghanekar. Anjali was a beautiful woman with around 5' 5" height, medium-built and wheatish complexion. In the media, she was well known for her vocabulary and probing skills. She had the reputation of being aggressive with her guests and was known to confuse the interviewee with both her barrage and baggage of questions.

Perhaps the whole country was thinking: *Would Rahul be able to face this woman?*

As the programme started, she took charge by greeting the TV viewers.

"Good evening, ladies and gentlemen and – since today is a special day – lovely kids! This evening, we have a special guest on our programme, a great personality who has amazed all of us through his actions. I must say, after learning about his recent achievements, I have become a great fan of this gentleman. He has always followed his heart more than his mind and achieved incredible success in all the fields he has explored!

"Ladies and gentlemen, join me in welcoming the technocrat and ex-CEO of one of the world's largest electronics company Gold Star Electronics... a loving and dedicated father, a teacher, and now a reformer of our education system, Mr Rahul Saxena."

As she opened the talk show, there was a big round of applause from the audience. She noticed that as she was introducing Rahul to the audience, the ferocity of the applause was increasing with every word she spoke, which showed Rahul's growing popularity even among the common people of the country.

Cameras zoomed on Rahul, who was sitting in front of Anjali. He was his usual self: composed, confident and energetic. He greeted the audience with folded hands and leaned forward to shake hands with Anjali. She proceeded with the interview.

"Welcome, Mr Saxena! You have developed the habit of making news. Last year you took the world by storm by inventing V-Office (Virtual Office) which made significant contribution in the growth of Gold Star. The effect of this invention was so great that the stocks of GS appreciated by about ten times in a few months' time. I was one of the beneficiaries of the spectacular increase in the stocks' value, and we were looking forward to earning some more when one fine day came the news that you had resigned. And, once again, you surprised the world by your totally unexpected move; you joined a small secondary school as a teacher. We are all very keen to know, why such a move?"

With her question, all eyes focused on Rahul, who smiled and said, "I would just describe this change as a gift showered on me by life. You will agree with me, I'm sure, that we are all driven by circumstances created by our lives. Like all of you, I am also a human being and life made me face a situation wherein I had to choose between a job and something that was much more precious in my life. I couldn't keep both so I chose that little precious thing, my son Sachin and his happiness."

At this revelation, there was another round of applause from the audience.

Anjali persisted, "But why did you choose to become a teacher? You could have handled the challenge posed by life in a different way, perhaps appoint the best tutor in town for your son. Why give up such a bright career and take up a secondary school teacher's job?"

Rahul counter-questioned, "Do you have kids?"

Anjali was startled, "Yes, I have a daughter."

"Fine. How old is she? And in which class is she studying?"

"She is eight years old and in the third standard."

"Now, if someone makes you an offer to choose between your daughter and ₹100 crore, what would you choose?"

"My daughter, of course," she replied promptly.

"That's exactly what I did. You see, a career is for the well-being of a family and not vice versa," he paused, gazing at the opposite wall of the studio for a few seconds and continued, "in my case, I had made a commitment to my wife."

Now interested, Anjali leaned forward and asked, "What commitment? Can you tell us?"

Again Rahul, lost in his thoughts, gazed at the wall. Anjali and the audience were becoming very curious, so they waited with baited breath, for Rahul to continue. But Rahul was lost in his thoughts; perhaps he had gone back to the past, and this delayed his response to Anjali's question.

Unable to wait longer, Anjali asked him once again, "Rahul, what was your commitment to your wife? Can you please tell us?"

Rahul came back to the present with a start, and said, "I had told my son 'It's okay to fail', but that didn't go well with my wife. So I had promised her that I will prepare my son in such a way that on the very foundation of failure, he would be able to build a very strong foundation of everlasting success!"

She retorted, "I can't believe it either. This statement of yours now takes my audience and me to the main question of the day: how could you as a father tell your own son to fail? Was that not a bit rash?" then she asked the audience, "what do you think, my friends?"

The audience reacted as expected, with a "Yes", "You are right, ma'am", and likewise.

Rahul smiled again, "That's exactly how my wife reacted after hearing my conversation with my son, Sachin. How could I be so irresponsible?"

He paused for a moment or two, and with a dazzling smile added, "All you beautiful ladies think alike. Great."

Anjali flashed a smile at this unexpected compliment.

"She too felt that I was an irresponsible father, but that's not the case. Let me explain the logic behind my telling Sachin that he could fail."

As he was saying this, there was pin drop silence in the audience, so as not to miss a single word.

Rahul continued, "You see, I was preparing him for bigger successes in life."

Rahul noticed Anjali's puzzled look, so he explained in detail. "See, as per human psychology, all our actions are driven by two fundamental factors: Desire to Gain and Fear of Loss. So for every action that we take, we either have the desire to gain something or a fear of losing something, which we want to prevent. Let us take your example, Anjali. You are working with City News because you are paid every month. With that money, you can lead a comfortable life and fulfil your needs and that of your family members. But, at the same time, you want to ensure that you and City News maintain a unique position in the competitive marketplace, so you work harder to ensure that your competitors do not score more points than City News.

"In other words, your consistent search for the best content for your company is driven by these two factors. Out of these two factors, fear of losing is more powerful. A fearful mind will only strive to achieve the results that are necessary to address the fear, like in the case of a student, he will work towards scoring marks that will help him pass the exams.

"But, this fear or negativity shackles the creativity of the mind, which is essential for achieving excellence. In other words, fear of loss acts as a big block in your journey towards excellence. Once you tackle the causes of fear and develop 'immunity' against failing, you can achieve results that can surprise you and the people around.

"Excellence comes when your mind is at the peak of its creativity. That happens when your mind is free from all sorts of negativity, which includes fear. Excellence is the result of your work which you enjoy doing, and you are passionate about continuously improving your own standard of performance. An excellence-seeker does not differentiate between work and relaxation. As a matter of fact, the more he works, the more he relaxes. Excellence is possible only when your mind is free from the fear of failure!"

As Rahul was speaking, Anjali and the audience were silent. Anjali's eyes had widened as if she had forgotten to blink, as if she had forgotten where she was! Suddenly she came to the 'present', and took hold of herself.

She said, "We have read about your teaching methods and, according to the information I have with me, the education ministry officials who had visited your school were extremely impressed at the depth of knowledge exhibited by your batch students. Earlier, the same students were considered failures or their performance was considered lower than average. How was this possible?"

"I personally believe that every human being has the same intelligence and capabilities. However, the difference in their comparative performance is primarily due to their interest in the subject matter, which is linked to the environment in which one operates and the exposure one gets. In case of the students of my batch, I never doubted their intelligence and capabilities so I focused on providing them with the right environment and wider exposure. I personally do not give much importance to the marks system, as right learning could automatically lead to better marks."

Anjali said, "My last question. Do you think what could be achieved by students of your batch can be achieved by any student anywhere in India or in any part of the world?"

Rahul was quick to reply, "Yes, of course. I believe any student who is given the right environment and guidance can achieve similar results. But remember, students are not solely responsible for their performance; it is the responsibility of teachers, parents and society. Jointly we have to create the right atmosphere so that their learning can blossom. We will have to stop putting children under pressure through high expectations, scolding and other pressure techniques or any other coercive methods to suppress them physically and mentally."

Rahul paused for some moments. It appeared he had become emotional.

"Every day we read in the newspaper of a teacher beating a student, which some times results in the loss of vision in one eye, or both, or loss of hearing, or even death of students. Every day, we expose our children to acts of terrorism and violence for one reason or the other. Just imagine what impact such events could have on the minds of our children. How much fearful their minds must be when they learn about such incidents. But, I am hopeful, if all of us take a conscious decision and become responsible and provide the right atmosphere to the children in our family and immediate environment, we can make a big difference not only in their academic performance, but we can create better world citizens. And we can make this world a livable place."

Rahul finished speaking. There was thunderous applause in the audience. Anjali thanked Rahul and closed the interview.

★   ★   ★

Far away from the studio where Rahul was interviewed, and his views were being appreciated by the city, there was one more person who appreciated every word spoken by Rahul in the interview. That person was Sheetal, Rahul's wife. Her eyes were swimming in tears.

"I completely misunderstood him! How could I have been so foolish as to misjudge my own husband? Perhaps, it was because of my arrogance and ego that I overlooked such a fine and capable person who has shone because of his qualities," she murmured.

She picked up the phone and dialled a number. After some time, she was in a coffee shop, with Madhuri sitting across her, in a posh five-star hotel in the vicinity.

She said sadly to Madhuri, "It was the biggest blunder of my life. I failed to recognize what a fine person he was, and always kept fighting with him. Now, in retrospect, I realize how mean I was when I had deserted him…" Sheetal could not speak further as her voice choked with emotion.

Madhuri got up from her chair and sat beside Sheetal, to console her. Sheetal raised her head and looked at Madhuri gratefully, her eyes too were full of tears.

The Attack

AS RAHUL'S INTERVIEW on TV ended, somewhere in the city another TV set was switched off. There sat another set of people who were not happy with the fame and recognition that Rahul was being showered with. This group had met at a distant location and were busy conversing about the unexpected success of Rahul's batch students, which in turn validated Rahul's teaching methodology.

This group was led by Politician Dikshit. Others present were Dikshit's son Shiv, teacher Meenakshi and the don Dagdu. They were all seated in a drawing room. Dikshit was very angry and bitter with Bhattacharya and Meenakshi.

"Bhattacharya spoiled everything. He made such tall claims but turned out to be a paper tiger!" Looking at Dagdu he continued, "Just see how a newcomer like Rahul has defeated him. Bhattacharya boasted about his rich experience of thirty years in teaching and whatnot. But still, see what happened? Where is he, by the way?"

His last words were in a very loud voice, and frightened Meenakshi.

He said, "Sir, please calm down. Now that the results are out, there's no point in remembering what Bhattacharya had claimed. As a matter of fact, on that day itself when the challenge was announced between Bhattacharya and Rahul, I had a feeling that Bhattacharya had less chances of winning."

Hearing this, Dikshit was taken aback, "Why do you say so? Why didn't you say this earlier?"

"Sir, that day when the challenge had been announced, I had seen Rahul and Madhuri in the school garden near the parking lot. Though I could not hear their conversation as I was watching them from a distance, but just by looking at Rahul's body language and the support he was getting from Madhuri, I got an inkling that he had bright chances of winning. Now I did not share it earlier as I was afraid of sharing my thoughts before the competition results were out, as Bhattacharya would not have liked it."

Dikshit noticed two things. First, Meenakshi had turned the tables to prove his innocence as well as his intelligence. This allowed Meenakshi to withdraw himself completely from the ongoing argument by saying he had envisaged Rahul's success from the first day itself. Simultaneously, Meenakshi was distancing himself from the competition and its results. And, second, Madhuri was close to Rahul.

Dikshit exhaled deeply. Dagdu was silent, listening to the ongoing conversation.

Now Dikshit turned to him, "Once again this guy Rahul has hurt us. We must do something about him."

Hearing this, Dagdu smiled wickedly, and said grimly, "I agree with you. Don't worry, we will do something about him."

They looked at each other and started laughing. Except Meenakshi, who was in a state of confusion.

★   ★   ★

It was 2.30pm. Bhattacharya had locked himself in his room, many a thought going through his mind. He was still not able to digest the fact that Rahul had been successful in the challenge and had transformed the students of his batch who had been consistently failing in previous exams.

Today, the same batch of students had performed brilliantly in front of the delegates and Principal Sir. 'Why only delegates? These students have proved to the world that my teachings and methods were wrong,' he thought. With such thoughts running over and over in his mind, Bhattacharya was reconciling with the fact that the new boy Rahul had demonstrated innovative teaching methods to the world.

These methods had immense potential in the fields of education and learning which could help not only students of Saraswati Vidhya Mandir but also students of the whole city, the country and the whole world. The more and more Bhattacharya thought about it, the more he appreciated the potential offered by Rahul's methods. He realized this was the second incident in his life that had affected him hugely.

Bhattacharya's mind drifted to the past. Images of a child lying on the bed surrounded by doctors treating him, a helpless father looking first at the doctor, then at the child and then beseechingly at the photo of a God, a teary-eyed mother with folded hands pleading to Bhattacharya to get back her son. With the passing of every moment, the images were becoming more prominent and clearer in front of his eyes, and then he started hearing even the cries of the mother. Tears filled his eyes, and finally spilled down his aged, wrinkled cheeks. The deep wrinkles indicated the hardships and the suffering that he must have faced in his life.

Abruptly he stood up and told himself, 'it happened to me

once, but I won't allow it to happen again.' He wiped away the tears with his palms and walked up to the wardrobe.

After some time, he went out of his house. There was a sparkle in his eyes and determination on his face as if he had found something.

★   ★   ★

Rahul was in a good mood that day; after all, there was reason to be happy, as his students had made him proud with their spectacular performance in front of the delegates. He himself was amazed at the hard work, deep interest in the subject and the passion for learning of his batch students.

He had taken all the students out for dinner, and had arranged a bus for the students to return home after the celebration. All, except Shankar, who was riding pillion. Since he had some work in Bandra, he would be dropping Shankar home, as the boy's house was on the way to Bandra. It was January but even then the skies had become dark and cloudy. The temperature had dropped and it appeared as if there would be a heavy downpour in some time. He stopped at the traffic signal and looked at the clouds. He thought, 'rain and in January?' But before he could realize, it had started to drizzle.

He turned back and asked Shankar, "Shall we stop somewhere and go later?"

"No, sir. I'm enjoying myself. Let's get wet."

"Are you sure? You won't catch a cold?"

"No, sir. Nothing will happen to me. I am strong enough."

"Okay then, let's go."

He raised the accelerator and turned his bike left, towards Bandra-Kurla Complex. The intensity of rainfall had increased, resulting in poor visibility of the road, particularly through the helmet that Rahul was wearing. However, since traffic was thin, he had no trouble driving the bike.

Suddenly he saw a white-coloured van come rushing in from one side; it screeched to a halt just in front of his bike. Rahul had to pump the bike's brakes hard to stop the two-wheeler. With great difficulty, he stopped his bike – but very close to the bonnet of the car. Even before he could figure out what was happening, four to five shadowy figures jumped out of the van, with stick-like things in their hands, and approached him slowly.

Sensing danger, Rahul put his bike on its stand and asked Shankar to run away and stay at a distance. Initially, Shankar objected but Rahul forced him to move away; Shankar did as told. Now Rahul was ready to face the threat. Incessant rain and dark clouds had made visibility very poor. Rahul could only see two images moving towards him from his right side. He took a defensive position, blocked the attack of the first image, and swung his leg in the air, kicking the face of the second image, who was thrown off. The shout of pain that emerged from the second attacker told Rahul that his kick had proved effective.

Making good use of these few minutes, Rahul punched the first attacker. Suddenly, Rahul felt an unbearable pain on his neck, and realized he had been hit from behind with a stick or some weapon. Standing in the same position, he looked back; he noticed a man wielding a hockey stick. Rahul swung a kick in the backward direction, and struck his attacker on the chest; he was thrown away, just about a few steps away. The attacker fell in a heap on the road, the intense pain in his chest immobilizing him.

This went on for about 7-8 minutes. Suddenly Rahul saw two attackers quietly moving to where Shankar was standing. He rushed towards them, and with this shift in Rahul's focus, he got distracted in the scuffle and fisticuffs that was going on with the thugs who had surrounded him. This gave the goons an opportunity and they struck him hard. Once again, he felt an unbearable pain shoot through his head. He gingerly placed his hand on his head, where he had been hit. He felt hot liquid trickling out; Rahul realized it was his blood.

Thereafter, Rahul was hit several times with sticks, and eventually, Rahul collapsed, blood oozing out of his wounds.

Leaving him on the road, the rest of the attackers picked up their injured companions and drove off in the van. Rahul lay on the roadside, unconscious and bleeding. Colourless raindrops that were falling on his body were flowing off his body, coloured red!

Poor Shankar stood where he was, trembling with fear, not knowing what to do. Suddenly, he gathered courage, rushed towards Rahul – and started screaming for help.

Tukaram was passing through the same road in his auto rickshaw. After he had overcome his addiction, he had become an auto rickshaw driver around Bandra and the western suburbs. He heard the screams and saw a man lying on the ground in an unconscious state. He had also seen the attackers speeding away in a white-coloured van. Despite the poor visibility, Tukaram could recognize one of the attackers. He wanted to go after the van and catch hold of him, but on second thoughts felt the need to save the life of the person lying on the road.

As he came near Rahul and the screaming child, he first recognized Shankar and then Rahul.

"Oh my God! This is Rahul Sir. I must take him to a hospital as fast as possible," he murmured as he halted his auto.

With Shankar's help, they lifted Rahul on the rickshaw, and Shankar too got in. Tukaram drove towards Mahajan Hospital.

After about 15 minutes, Rahul was admitted in the hospital of Dr Amit Mahajan.

★   ★   ★

The OPD staff swung into action at the hospital. Four boys came out with a stretcher and took Rahul inside the Emergency Ward, while the support staff telephoned Dr Amit Mahajan who came running down as soon as he was informed.

Amit checked Rahul, and informed the attending hospital staff that a lot of blood had been lost. In the meantime, the Emergency staff informed the RMO as well, on Dr Mahajan's orders. As Amit continued with his examination, he noted the deep cut on his head – someone had hit him with something heavy, possibly an iron rod or a hockey stick – and Rahul's right arm was fractured. There was a wound in the stomach too, caused by a sharp weapon. Fortunately, it was on the side, so his intestines and other vital organs were clean of any injury. But due to the severity of the wounds and delay in getting Rahul to the hospital, a large amount of blood was lost. Dr Amit asked the RMO to take Rahul to the Operation Theatre, and his team of doctors started treating Rahul.

Soon, news of the attack on Rahul spread, and people started gathering outside the OT – some members of the school staff, Principal Sir, Madhuri, Sheetal, and Sachin, students of Rahul's batch and their parents, and other school students. The security staff of the hospital reported the case to the police, as such an attack was a police case and, to be on the safe side, for some help to control the crowd which was increasing in size with every passing moment.

Police Inspector Javed Khan entered the hospital gate in his jeep. Seeing the crowd, he called the police station for backup, and made his way to the OT with two constables. Recognizing Sheetal, he walked up to her.

Giving her a slight smile, he said, "I'm sorry to hear about the attack on Mr Saxena. He is such a fine gentleman that I still can't believe that he has enemies who can beat him up so brutally. Do you suspect anyone?"

Wiping her eyes, Sheetal shook her head; no, she had no idea of who could have done this to Rahul. Khan then approached Madhuri – she too had been crying – and repeated the same question but she too could not name anyone.

As Khan went about his duty, talking to all those present outside the OT to get some information on Rahul's attack, Dr Amit came out, still in his scrubs.

He went up to Sheetal and Sachin and said, "Rahul has been hit badly. He had lost substantial blood by the time he was brought to the hospital. We must thank God that we have been able to save his life. However, because of the massive injury on his head, right now he is in coma. We will do a CT scan, and by evening we will know his exact condition," and after updating them, he went back to the OT.

Hearing this, Sheetal felt the ground swaying beneath her, and she fell down unconscious. Madhuri rushed towards her, calling for help. Those present there, and two nurses who were on duty, came running to her assistance. Sheetal was immediately moved to the OPD for treatment.

As the hospital staff took away Sheetal, Madhuri moved towards Sachin, feeling sorry for the poor boy, who was clearly in a daze. First his dad was attacked and injured, and he was now in coma. Then, his mum was unconscious. Seeing Madhuri coming towards him, he walked up to her, and embraced her.

Crying, he put his head on her shoulder, and mumbled, "Ma'am, what will happen now?"

Controlling her own emotions, Madhuri said, "Don't worry Sachin, everything will be alright. See, I'm here. We will settle everything right."

Seeing that Sachin was inconsolable, she continued, "You're a brave boy. Don't you remember all that your father had said about courage? This is a temporary phase; it will pass. Your parents are being treated here, in this hospital, which is among the best in the city, and by Dr Mahajan, who is one of the best doctors in India. Now we have to put our faith in the doctor and the Almighty… they will set everything right for us."

She made him sit down on one of the chairs near the OT, and brought him some drinking water.

In spite of putting up a brave face in front of Sachin, Madhuri was terribly upset from within. 'Who could have attacked Rahul? He is such a gentleman, then how come he was beaten so brutally,' she asked herself, over and over again.

The same question was baffling Inspector Javed Khan as well; having drawn a blank in his preliminary investigation of this case, he too was puzzling over it again and again: who could have attacked Rahul?

*   *   *

Javed Khan was sitting in his chamber; he had gone over his notes on the Rahul Saxena case several times and had spoken to a few hospital staff, but he was still in the dark. Sepoy Salunkhe knocked on the door of his chamber.

"Yes, come in."

Salunkhe entered the chamber and said, "Sir, someone named Tukaram wants to meet you in connection with the attack on Rahul Saxena."

271

Excited, Javed Khan stood up, and said, "What are you waiting for? Send him in fast."

After a few minutes, Tukaram entered his chamber. He greeted Khan with folded hands. "Namaskar, sir."

Javed nodded and asked him to sit down on one of the chairs that were kept in his chamber. Tukaram sat down, and looked at the inspector nervously.

Javed asked, "How do you know Rahul Saxena?"

"My son studies in his class," Tukaram replied. "He is not just a teacher, but a saint, a miracle man, who not only transformed my son's life but also took me out of the hell I was living in."

Tukaram then briefly told Khan that he had been an alcoholic for many years, that his family's fortunes were ruined by his addiction, how his son, Shankar's, childhood had been adversely impacted by Dagdu Dada, and how Rahul had appeared as saviour and saved Shankar from Dagdu's clutches. Javed now remembered Rahul's encounter with Dagdu and that with his intervention, Dagdu was put behind bars – but was later released against the bail order.

"So do you mean to say Dagdu attacked Rahul?"

"I'm not very sure, but my own assessment is that he must be involved. I can't say confidently, but on the night of the attack, when I was rescuing Rahul Sir, one of the fleeing images seemed to be Dagdu."

Javed got up from his desk. "Thanks, Tukaram. You may go. If required, I will call you. We will now get into action."

He strode out of his chamber and asked Sepoy Salunkhe to get two more constables. He sat in the police jeep and instructed the driver, "Rajiv Gandhi Nagar."

The Other Side of a Human

NEWS CHANNELS WERE abuzz with the breaking news. Rahul Saxena's attackers had been identified, and were arrested: Dagdu, the local don, the politician Dikshit, and his son. Panels on TV news channels also discussed whether Bhattacharya and Meenakshi were involved in the attack or not.

Anjali informed Principal Sir of the breaking news. He looked at his watch; it was 4.30pm. He went to the AV room, accompanied by Anjali, and switched on the TV. And was shocked at what he heard, at what the news channels claimed to be true.

"Impossible," he said. "This cannot be true."

"Sir, I also hope that it's not true, but we can't say unless we get into details. In today's world, nothing is impossible."

Principal Daruwala stared at her for some time and said, "In that case, I want to meet both of them right now. Can you call them?" then he remembered something and added, "call Madhuri as well. She has always believed in and supported Rahul. I would also like her to know the truth."

Anjali nodded and went out of the AV room.

After about an hour, Bhattacharya, Meenakshi and Madhuri arrived. Bhattacharya was looking pale and tired, as if he had not slept and eaten properly for some days. Madhuri too looked tensed and exhausted. She had come because of the call from Anjali but her mind was elsewhere. She kept looking at her wristwatch again and again, as if she was in a hurry to leave the place as soon as possible.

They were waiting in Principal Sir's room. He had gone on a round. After they had waited for around 15 minutes, the principal returned to his room. All three of them stood up, and greeted him.

"Good evening, sir."

"Good evening," he responded, and taking his seat behind the large imposing desk, continued, "I'm reciprocating your greeting as it is customary to do so. But, as you know, it is not a good time for our school as one of our colleagues and my friend Rahul has been hospitalized, and in coma, for the past three days."

As he spoke, the principal looked at all of them as if he was scanning their minds, trying to read their thoughts.

He cleared his throat and continued, "While we are struggling with this crisis, TV channels are abuzz with news of the involvement of some senior teachers of our school in the attack on Rahul. Even in my dream, I cannot think that a person, who has been teaching lessons of calmness and tolerance to students, can get involved in such a heinous act. Mr Bhattacharya and Meenakshi, while the police will do their job, I want to know the truth from your mouth."

Meenakshi spoke first, "Sir, I was friendly with Bhattacharya Sir and I also supported him in this competition, but that's all.

As soon as the results were announced, I withdrew from it all. In fact, I wasn't present in Mumbai on the day of the attack, as I had to go to my hometown in Tamil Nadu. You can check with Anjali Ma'am, I had put a request for leave during the same week."

The principal looked at Anjali, who nodded in affirmation.

Then Roshan Daruwala looked at Bhattacharya sternly.

Bhattacharya understood that Principal Sir doubted his integrity, and was fairly certain that he was involved in the attack on Rahul.

He began quietly, "I did do some things which may have raised a doubt in your mind, but I can swear in the name of the Almighty that I am not involved in this crime. I accept that I did grave injustice to Rahul and Madhuri by selecting all the bright students for my batch and the failures in Rahul's batch, so that he would not win the competition. I did not live up to their trust! I felt extremely bad and guilty when Rahul told me that in his heart he regarded me as an elder brother! I could not believe that there could be a person like him, who had such love and respect for even his competitor, who was all out to ruin his efforts and career," and Bhattacharya burst into tears.

The principal was aware of the extent of Bhattacharya's role in selecting the batch students. However, even in this critical situation, he could not resist asking, "But why did you do that? Did Rahul know about this? And still he allowed you to carry on with your trick?"

Bhattacharya told the whole story of how he had inadvertently played into the hands of Dikshit who misused his impatience to push their personal agenda of ousting Rahul from the school. He also informed the principal that Dikshit had been eyeing Madhuri and he was very upset with Rahul since Madhuri had started liking Rahul and she was getting closer to Rahul.

"But three days have passed and you didn't visit the hospital even once to check how Rahul is doing!" Madhuri remarked in a bitter tone.

"That's not true, I went near the hospital... gates... at least three times but didn't dare enter as that hospital has taken away a lot from me. I didn't want to lose one more beloved person, so though I went near the gates, I turned back as my past wounds are still raw."

Bhattacharya's voice had started trembling, but nevertheless he continued, "This hospital has taken away my life from me, what you are seeing today is just a corpse dragging itself because death hasn't heeded my repeated pleas!"

Everyone except Madhuri, who did not seem to be impressed, was shocked at this statement from Bhattacharya.

Tears rolling down his cheeks, Bhattacharya proceeded. "Around 15 years ago, I was also a blessed father. My son Rohan was just on the threshold of his teenage years. He was in Class VII. Rohan was a bright student and a very sensitive child. He loved cricket and every Sunday I had no option but to play cricket with him. He would wake me up early morning, and push his mother for breakfast. In a way, he used to create an atmosphere that we loved in our hearts, but outwardly we displayed our displeasure and resistance to his actions."

There was a slight smile on his face, as Bhattacharya described the events of the past. 'What a contrast life offers to us human beings,' Madhuri thought while observing the sad and tearful Bhattacharya who now had a smile on his face while remembering his son.

Madhuri forced herself to concentrate on what Bhattacharya was saying.

"Around 8.30am every Sunday, we would be on the ground. He loved batting, so he would play every known trick to bat first. Just to tease him, I would fight with him and insist that I would bat first, but in my mind, I was pleased just to see him energetic and jovial.

"Our strong bonding kept his mother very happy. While we played, she would cook a sumptuous meal, which we relished on Sunday afternoons, after our game was over. We would often compete who could eat more fish or more rice and I would allow him to win, even if that meant I had to remain hungry! We had wonderful days, what a fulfilling life!"

It seemed as if Bhattacharya had gone back to that wonderful time in his life; everyone listened to him silently.

"But our happiness did not continue for long. On one Sunday, after hitting a shot, Rohan shouted out in pain; he could not stand and fell down. We rushed him to our family doctor, who thought the pain was due to some gastric problem, and he gave him a painkiller and an injection. The pain subsided and we returned home. That day he was very tired, so he slept. After that day, for a few days, this pain episode was forgotten and we became busy living our routine life. But that relief did not last long.

"Some days later, he again complained of pain in the same area, so my family doctor advised us to consult a specialist."

'Why is Bhattacharya Sir getting exhausted after talking for just about 15 minutes?' Madhuri wondered, and offered him a glass of water.

When the senior teacher paused a while, she asked Bhattacharya, "Sir, are you okay? You look worn-out."

Bhattacharya gave her a feeble smile, as if to say that it was perhaps because of the heavy load that he had been carrying for so many years now.

After drinking some water, Bhattacharya resumed, "We went to a gastroenterologist in Dr Amit Mahajan's hospital. He examined Rohan and recommended a series of tests. We carried out all those tests.

"I still remember the day when the reports of those tests were announced to us. It was as if the sky had fallen on our heads.... Rohan was diagnosed with cancer in his kidney. The disease had spread in his left kidney and the doctor suggested an emergency operation. We were stunned, did not know what to do. How does one react to a sudden critical situation? As father and head of the family, my situation was even worse; I had to manage my sinking feelings and thoughts and at the same time put up a brave face to my wife, whose condition cannot be described in words."

Bhattacharya could not control himself, and wept like a child. The atmosphere in the principal's office had become heavy and sad. Everyone's eyes were full of tears.

"Doctors operated on Rohan, and removed his left kidney. After a few days, he was back home from the hospital, and my wife and I were living with the hope that even though one kidney was lost, we still had our son. So we started taking extra care of him. Earlier, he went to school by the school bus, but now she would drop him to school, wait outside the school while his classes were going on, sometimes in the hot sun, feed him the home-cooked food in recess time and bring him back from school. I had asked her several times not to take so much of strain on herself, but she never listened. Her son was more precious than her own life!"

Bhattacharya was drained by now; his breathing had become heavy and uneven.

Worried, Principal Sir said, "Mr Bhattacharya, you are not well, please take rest. We will talk some other day."

But Bhattacharya refused, a slight smile on his face, "Sir, don't worry about me. Nothing will happen to me. Let me finish my story."

He looked at the principal with pleading eyes. Principal Sir nodded in affirmation, and so he continued.

"A year passed in this way. We thought that finally God has been kind to us. But we were wrong. One night, when we were all sleeping, Rohan suddenly woke up, and started crying. I rushed him to a doctor, who could not identify the reason for his pain. I took him to the hospital, where doctors again carried out a number of tests on him. Once again, we were entrapped in the circle of doctors, tests, prescriptions, medicines and hospital. While all this was going on, he was suffering from pain which with heavy doses of painkillers had taken a toll on his health. He was losing weight. As a side effect of the medicines, he also started losing hair. Those were very difficult days for my wife and me, as we had to see Rohan's health steadily deteriorate, but were unable to do anything. I don't know how many times, but at least several times in a day, I prayed to God that he should transfer my son's illness to me and free him from the pain and suffering, but all my prayers and wishes went in vain!"

Bhattacharya's tears had dried now, perhaps even exhausted, but the pain in his voice, heavy breathing and the trembling in his voice still continued. There was pin drop silence in the room. Madhuri looked around, she saw lines of deep sorrow on everyone's face; they were all stupefied.

Bhattacharya continued, "I still remember that day, when the doctor showed us the reports of all the tests. Rohan's second kidney was also damaged. The doctor said it was an emergency situation, so they put him on dialysis. Now his movements were also restricted. The boy who would play sports for 5-6 hours a day was now confined within the four walls of the hospital, mostly tied down to the bed.

"While all this was going on, under the stress of his pain and suffering, one important thing I omitted was my finances. My bank balance had started depleting."

He looked first at Principal Sir and then at Madhuri and said, "You know what we get in this job. Hardly enough to make two ends meet in a month and then such a major illness. But I didn't lose hope, and when I had exhausted all our cash and ornaments, I encashed all deposits in the provident fund. When that was not enough, I put my house on mortgage and took a loan from a private company. We did all this, but still there was no sign of his recovery. The doctor called us and said his second kidney was badly damaged – cannot be saved – and they recommended an operation to remove the second kidney as well. They also asked us to look out for a donor who would donate a kidney to save my son's life!

"Without wasting any time, I told the doctor to take my kidney and save my son... take both if needed!" Bhattacharya paused and sipped some water.

With tears rolling down his cheek, Bhattacharya folded his hands and said, as if he was reliving that old moment, years back, with the doctor sitting in front of him, "Doctor, please take my whole body and everything I own, but, give me, in return my son's life and good health. The doctor asked me to be ready for the operation.

"After carrying out some tests to check compatibility, both Rohan and I were operated on the same day. My kidney was removed and transplanted in his body. Before my surgery and after I regained consciousness, I continuously prayed to God to transfer all his pains and illness to me. May the wellness of my kidney spread health in my son's body. By this time, my wife and I had forgotten ourselves. We didn't remember if we had slept or eaten. I was by his bedside in the hospital and she was at home. She would visit him only in the evenings. The guards told me later that she would be present at the hospital gate every day at around 3pm.

"In this way, around six months passed. We again became hopeful and I was thankful to God that, Rohan had a new lease of life. However, that was only temporary. His body rejected my kidney and again the same series of pain, tests, medicines, doctors and hospital continued, but this time we could not save him. One morning he didn't wake up from his sleep. He was no more!"

Bhattacharya sobbed uncontrollably while saying this; his ordeal and anguish moved everyone to tears. Principal Sir too had not been able to control his emotions; he had moved near the window, and wiped his eyes openly now.

Some minutes later, they quietened down. Anjali offered water to everyone; and after checking with the others, ordered tea and biscuits. After tea had been served, they were all seated and composed, and Principal Sir was back in his own chair, Bhattacharya resumed; he too had become calm now.

"That day, as Rohan lay on the floor of my house, I told him I did everything for you and now when it was your turn to perform, you ditched us. From that day, I lost confidence in people around me. All of you might have noticed I had become quite acerbic in my behaviour with not only students but with the staff too."

He looked at Principal Sir and said, "Sir, even you might have noticed the bitterness in my nature. I have misbehaved with you even, several times, but you showed generosity and did not make any issue out of it."

He looked around at all of them, with gratitude and said apologetically, "Due to my painful experiences in life, I might have become nasty with everyone around," then looking at Madhuri and Anjali, he said, "with you, the staff and, more importantly, students."

He stopped, gazed outside the window as if he had forgotten that he had been speaking, and was in the middle of his narration and explanation. He resumed talking after Madhuri gently reminded him.

"Then Rahul joined our school. A completely different person, with a completely different approach and thinking. His attitude and perspective were very different... he was patient, understanding, and friendly with everyone. I felt many times that he was right but every time I tried to change my thoughts, my past overwhelmed me... and came as a big hindrance. I did the best for my son but still he left us all alone in this world. I gave him all that I had but still..."

He couldn't complete the sentence; he was again overcome with emotions, and broke down. All eyes in that room were filled with tears, no one was in a mood to talk or listen. Madhuri looked out of the window; it had become dark outside. She felt as if everything had come to a standstill, including time, which too had stopped!

Unleashing the Power of Faith

IT WAS THE tenth day since Rahul's attack. His condition remained the same. Media coverage and interest about his condition had lessened. People had become busy with their lives, the city of Mumbai was again back on track.

Even in Saraswati Vidhya Mandir, students and other teachers had become busy in their daily routine. After all, they had a reason to as exams were fast approaching. But for a few people, life had changed permanently due to Rahul's current condition. Hope was slowly waning among the students and parents of his batch – and for Madhuri too.

Madhuri was sitting in the staffroom, when Gautam, Shankar, Murali, Sapna and Ameya knocked on the door.

"May we come in, ma'am?"

Madhuri was surprised to see them there, especially as their classes were still going on, so instead of responding to their greetings, she asked them sternly, "Don't you have classes now?

Why are you roaming about at this time?"

Hesitantly, they looked at each other, as if each one was waiting for the other to speak. Madhuri was waiting for a reply so she looked at each one of them questioningly, one eyebrow raised. Madhuri was quite loving and friendly with all the students, so her gesture made them smile a bit.

Gautam gathered some courage and said, "Ma'am, how is Rahul Sir?"

"Gautam, I don't know the details, but still in the same condition. He is still in coma."

"Ma'am, when will he recover and come to school? We are all waiting for him to come back, and be with us," said Sapna.

Madhuri was touched by their sensitivity and care for their favourite teacher. She felt tears gathering, but forced herself to speak normally to the children. Seeing their tensed faces, she didn't want to upset them any further than they already were.

Forcing herself to smile, she assured them, "Don't worry, Rahul Sir will be fine and will be with all of us soon. But you must prepare for your exams. Please go back to your class and concentrate on your studies."

Gautam said, "Ma'am, when Sir is in such a condition, we are not able to study. Forget about studying, we can't even concentrate."

Madhuri got up from her chair and asked them, "Is this how you will contribute to Rahul Sir's efforts, to all the hard work he put behind all of you? Will you fail him?"

Tears in his eyes, Gautam replied, "Ma'am, we are not able to focus on our studies. Every time I sit with a book in my hand, I see Sir's bandaged face. I feel like crying, so how do I study?"

Madhuri understood what they were going through. She

asked them all to follow her. They came out in the open and walked towards the school ground. As they reached a big tree located in one corner of the ground, she stopped and asked the children to sit down on a nearby bench.

When they had sat down, Madhuri asked, noting their gloomy faces, "Do you all love Rahul Sir?"

"Yes, ma'am, we all love him very much," they replied in a chorus.

"Then, you must walk on the path shown by Rahul Sir. I agree, right now he is in the hospital and he is not around. But remember, he is not going to remain in the hospital for long. What will you tell him when he returns after 10–15 days, you all did nothing? You did not study hard but wasted time? Do you think he is going to like it?" Madhuri stopped and looked at the children.

They were intently listening to her, capturing every word with great interest. Some stared back at her; some nodded their heads in agreement. So, Madhuri answered her own question.

"Certainly, he is not going to like it. He will never accept the fact that his students did not perform well in their studies. When he is not around, it is our responsibility to live by the examples he has set for all of us. And, get results matching his expectations, if he was around. That is the love, care and right gratitude to our Sir."

The children were in deep thought, she saw. After a few minutes, Gautam stood up, quite excited.

"Ma'am, you are right. We must fulfil our promise to Rahul Sir. We will do our best, we will not let down the confidence he has on us," then he looked at the other children and asked, "what do you say? Do you agree with me?"

Although they were close to tears, perhaps because of Rahul's condition, they looked excited and jumped up eagerly from their seat, and shouted in unison, "Yes! We will do our best to get an excellent result in the coming exams."

Then some of them abruptly sat down on the bench and started sobbing disconsolately. Madhuri could not control her emotions either, and she embraced some students and let her tears flow.

This was a strange situation! The environment was one of depression, but it was also one charged with enthusiasm. While they were desolate at their dear Rahul Sir lying in coma in the hospital, they were scared as well at his absence at such a critical time of their life, with examinations looming up in the near future.

On the other hand, they were filled with determination and enthusiasm for the opportunity to validate Rahul Sir's approach towards students, his innovative teaching methodology, his courage to explore talent even among students with a poor track record. His faith and belief in treating all students equally, and giving each one of them a chance to prove that everyone is born with the same intelligence and capabilities, motivated them. If the right atmosphere is created, any student will perform well.

And these innocent, tender minds did not know manipulation, adjustment or compromise. Their minds were as pure as the water streaming out of the earth at the mouth of River Ganges, which knows no obstacle, no hindrance or no limitation. Driven by the faith in their teacher's advice, now they were ready to flow in the Ganges of knowledge and learning. Unstoppable, with high energy and enthusiasm – and with the Belief that they can't go wrong; they can't *fail*.

Happy Comeback

IT WAS THE thirty-ninth day of Rahul's hospitalization. Sachin had made it his daily schedule of attending school in the morning and remaining by Rahul's bedside for the rest of the day. He would sit on a sofa near Rahul's bed, take out his books, and study.

It was evening. After finishing her work at school, Madhuri arrived at the hospital. This was her routine for most of the days, unless she had to complete some urgent work. She slowly opened the door and peeped into Rahul's room. Madhuri could not bear to look at Rahul, with all those tubes, beeping machines and drip, as tears would fill her eyes. She felt very helpless as she could neither see Rahul in such a state, and nor was she able to do anything about it.

She removed her footwear outside the door and came inside. Sachin was engrossed in his studies.

"Good evening, Sachin!"

She greeted Sachin in a very soft voice.

Sachin looked up and exclaimed, "Good evening, ma'am! Nice to see you. When did you come?"

"Just now... how are you?"

287

"Sachin replied a bit sadly, "How do I look, ma'am?"

"You look good, though a little unhappy, which is understandable because of Rahul Sir's current state of health. You are a good boy and I don't want to lecture you but, Sachin, our challenge now is to keep up the spirit of Rahul Sir's teachings, his dream that all students of his batch perform to the best of their capabilities. And, it is because of you that he took the biggest decision of his life, of giving up a very lucrative career and teaching in our school. So now, it is your turn to reciprocate.

"You are all grown up now. When your dad is in such a condition, you have to become not only your own guardian but also of your family. We all, and primarily you, have to face this challenging time with a high amount of courage and patience. So carry on with your studies in such a way that just by hearing how well you all have done, Rahul Sir will wake up from his deep sleep," Madhuri tried to pump up Sachin's mood.

But while she was speaking, her eyes turned moist. She didn't want to show her anxiety to Sachin, so she looked down.

Sachin noticed her nervousness, and with a little smile, he pointed out, "Ma'am, on one hand you are telling me to be courageous, but on the other hand you yourself are scared. Ma'am, look, your own eyes have turned teary... you are crying... but look at me. Look at my eyes, you won't find even a drop of tear."

Madhuri looked up.

Tears were rolling down Sachin's cheeks, yet he was saying, "Do I look scared? Am I crying? Not at all. I want to set an example to everyone around that we have to live by example, of what my dad has taught us."

Hearing Sachin, Madhuri was overwhelmed by her own emotions, and tried her utmost to control her feelings, when an unfamiliar sound that seemed to come from inside the room, caught her attention. She asked Sachin to stop talking and listened carefully again. She again heard that noise. Now she could make out it was coming from behind.

She turned around. She didn't know how to react, her senses were stunned for some time. Rahul was murmuring something. 'Oh my God,' she told herself, 'Rahul seems to be gaining consciousness.' She looked at Sachin who was also surprised and excited to see Rahul's hand and fingers moving jerkily.

He exclaimed, "Ma'am, finally God has listened to our prayers. Dad seems to be regaining consciousness. I'll call the doctor!" and he ran out of the room.

Madhuri's happiness knew no bounds as she saw Rahul finally 'waking up'. First, she folded her hands, quickly thanked God for the miracle and then rushed near Rahul.

"Rahul, Rahul... open your eyes, Rahul," she tried waking him up.

Rahul was trying hard to open his eyes, and slowly he opened his eyes. Then he saw Madhuri and smiled at her.

"Hey Mad, how are you?"

That was the name by which he called her, and had kept it to himself so far. Rahul had never uttered it in front of Madhuri.

Feeling shy, she smiled at Rahul and said, "I'm very happy to see you. How are you?"

Struggling to get up, Rahul asked in a barely audible voice, "Where am I?" then looked around and asked, "is this a hospital? How did I come here?"

Madhuri replied, "Don't stress yourself, I'll tell you everything but not now. Please rest."

Rahul put his head down, back on the pillow, and closed his eyes.

Within moments, Sachin entered the room with a doctor and nurse. The doctor examined Rahul with his stethoscope, and also checked the readings on the medical equipment kept around Rahul's bed.

He turned to Madhuri and smiled, "It's great that Mr Saxena is out of coma; he will be weak for some time now, so we should allow him to take rest. I am giving him an injection; he will sleep for 2-3 hours, after that he will be in a better condition to talk to you."

He patted the excited Sachin, and left the room.

Sachin asked Madhuri if he could use her phone. Madhuri gave her phone to Sachin.

He dialled Sheetal and said, "Mum, Dad is out of coma now."

"Some time back," his eyes were full of tears and voice trembled with excitement as he replied to her questions.

"Yes, Mum, God is great. I got my dad back."

"Yes, Mum, Madhuri Miss was with me when Dad came out of the coma."

"Yeah, Mum, come quickly, I'm waiting for you."

Sachin disconnected the phone, and returned it to Madhuri, grinning from ear to ear.

Madhuri called up Principal Sir and told him about Rahul gaining consciousness. The news that Rahul Saxena had come out of coma, spread like wildfire. Joy and relief filled the city.

★   ★   ★

It was visiting time in the hospital. The visitor's room was full of people eagerly waiting to get a glimpse of Rahul.

Dr Amit Mahajan entered the visitor's room and said, "Dear

friends, I am the dean of this hospital. I am also a friend and fan of Rahul Saxena like you all, but we have to take some precautions such as protect Rahul from any infections. We will allow only a few staff members of the school and his family to meet him personally. The rest get to see him through the TV set that we will install in this room."

Ameya came forward and said, "Dad, please allow students of our batch to meet Rahul Sir. We have exams from tomorrow, so we will not get time to meet him once our exams start."

Suddenly a voice said, "You don't need to make any effort to meet me, I'm always there, for all of you."

It was Rahul with a broad smile on his face.

There was a cheer in the crowd, and his well-wishers practically went berserk seeing Rahul fit and fine. "Rahul Sir!", "Rahul Sir!" they all chanted. Much to Dr Amit's chagrin, Rahul came inside the room and shook hands with everyone. Then Dr Amit requested the visitors to disperse and vacate the room. They cooperated and trooped out within a few minutes.

Now only Rahul's batch students remained in the room.

Rahul looked at them all and said, "What are you all doing here? I understand your final exams start from tomorrow, so you had better prepare for them."

The children were overwhelmed at seeing Rahul in person.

Gautam came forward and said, "Sir, our performance in the exams is not dependent on last-minute preparations, and we have all prepared well for the exams. We just wanted to see you once. Now that we have met you, we will take your leave. Wish you good luck, sir," he said and handed Rahul a big bouquet of flowers.

After everyone left, Rahul returned to his room, accompanied by Dr Amit, and lay down on his bed, feeling very weak.

The D-Day

THE NEXT THREE months saw a flurry of activities in the school. And then came D-Day… Results Day. All the children waited anxiously for their results. The results were soon declared – and so was that of the competition between the teams of Rahul and Bhattacharya, which was there for all to see. All the students in Rahul's batch had demonstrated excellence; Bhattacharya's students too had scored better than their earlier performance. So in a way, the competition had helped all the students, but in the case of Gautam, Shankar, Murali, Ameya, Sapna and other batch students of Rahul, this experience proved to be the turning point of their lives!

More than the students, their parents were happy, particularly parents like Tukaram and Shantabai, Ramakrishnan – Murali's father – and Gautam's uncle and aunt, who had lost hope for Gautam.

News channels and newspapers were covering the news in detail, of how a batch of students who had a very poor track record had made it to the toppers' list in the city's school.

Madhuri's happiness knew no bounds, as the results validated Rahul's teaching methods. While walking towards her room, she felt as if she was walking on clouds.

Someone called her from behind, "Good morning, ma'am!"

She looked back; Gautam was walking towards her.

She smiled and responded, "Good morning, Gautam!"

Gautam touched her feet. Madhuri held him by his shoulders and hugged him.

"Congratulations, Gautam, for your amazing performance in the exams! I myself can't believe you are the same Gautam who used to fail earlier. You have made me proud with your hard work. Keep it up!"

Hearing such rare words of appreciation from his favourite teacher, Gautam's face blossomed like a flower.

With a broad smile on his face, he said, "Ma'am, I'm the same Gautam who used to fail. Whatever I and the other students of our batch have achieved is because of yours and Rahul Sir's hard work – and Rahul Sir's teachings! You guided us so nicely that even a dumb person like me has changed," then looking around, he asked, "have you seen Rahul Sir?"

Madhuri said, "No, I have not met him since morning. Why are you asking?"

Gautam said, "We batch students wanted to meet Rahul Sir and show him our results. Would you like to join us, ma'am?"

"Certainly. He must be in the staffroom. Let's go."

As they started walking towards the staffroom, other students of Rahul's batch also joined them. As the group walked along, other students joined them, some out of curiosity, and some out of a desire to meet Rahul and learn a few things.

The Pleasant Dilemma

PRINCIPAL ROSHAN DARUWALA was confused: how should he react? He was holding an envelope in his hand, on which was embossed the emblem of the Government of India, New Delhi. He again opened the envelope, took out the letter and re-read it. Then, he pressed the bell on his desk to call the office boy. When the office boy knocked on the door, the principal asked him to bring him a cup of tea. Next, Principal Sir picked up the phone and asked Anjali to come to his office. When Anjali entered the room, he handed her the envelope quietly. She took it, removed the letter from within, and read it.

As she was reading, her expression reflected her increasing delight. By the time, she had finished reading the letter, she was beaming with joy.

She exclaimed, "This is great news, sir!"

She looked at Principal Roshan, who looked a tad worried. She couldn't understand why he was so perturbed, and asked, "Are you not pleased with the news?"

"Yes, I'm happy but I'm also unhappy."

"What do you mean?"

"I'm happy for Rahul, but when I think about my school which needs him, I'm not so happy with the contents of this letter. I'm being honest about my feelings, Anjali. I feel Rahul must stay with us and contribute more in the growth of this institution," Principal Sir said with a bit of sadness in his voice.

"But this is great news, not only for Rahul Sir, who has seen a lot more successes than what is written in this letter, but also for our school. We should be very proud that he is being offered such an important role and given the chance to shape the lives of students across the country," she said in excitement, and then realizing Principal Sir's point, added, "I understand your point, but Rahul Sir's expertise is like a fragrance. You can hold the bottle containing perfume but you really can't hold on to the fragrance!"

"Yes, I see the logic in what you are saying. Well, let's talk to Rahul and share the good news with him."

Anjali went out and asked the office boy to call Rahul.

After some time, Rahul entered the principal's office. Roshan handed him the letter. He read it but did not show much enthusiasm.

"Are you not happy about receiving such an invitation?"

"Sir, you know why I have joined your school... I am here only for my son."

Principal Sir said, "Yes, I know, but this is a big honour. It is an acknowledgement of your talent and skills. Plus, it gives you an opportunity to shape the lives of millions of students across India," then he added, "I feel, you must take it."

"I will need to think about it. Can I confirm after a couple of days?"

"Sure, there's no hurry. Think about it."

Rahul quietly shut the door as he walked out of Principal Sir's room.

The Proposal

DAVID BROWN, CHAIRMAN of Gold Star Electronics, was sitting in his chamber, his laptop open, frowning at the company's annual results. He was disgusted with the company's performance. He opened the page that gave details of the company's performance in the stock market. The company's stocks had been consistently marching southwards in the last four quarters.

He set aside the laptop, thought for a while, and then spoke over the phone.

"Can you come to my room?"

After some time, there was a knock on his door.

"Come on in, Peter."

Peter Hoffman entered the room and sat on the single sofa, which was kept in David's chamber. David was still in deep thought; he waited for David to speak.

David looked at Peter and pushed his laptop towards him, "You must have seen this," he murmured.

Peter looked at the laptop screen, opened some more files and then said, "Yes, I have."

"What do you think?" David asked him.

"Bad. We need to do something drastically different to improve," opined Peter.

"Exactly my sentiments. Tell me, what can we do?"

"Bring back the man who created history by taking the company's valuations to the sky," Peter paused and added, "just a year back."

"Will he come?"

"Not sure. But, if you make the right kind of offer, he will, I suppose. Money has an amazing power, you know."

David took a deep breath and thought for some time. After a while, he asked, "Can you handle this?"

"Yes. I can. What are the terms?"

"No budget for getting him. You decide with him. But you must get him. We can't afford this kind of performance for too long. You will report to me directly. I will be available 24x7 for this activity. Don't hesitate to call me any time, any day."

Peter nodded in agreement.

"All right, Peter, that'll be all... you may get back to work."

Peter got up and went out of the room.

Teacher: A Hapless God?

IT WAS THE Annual Day of Saraswati Vidhya Mandir. Generally, it was held in May, to coincide with the results of the board exams. Students were felicitated on this day – those who had done well in the SSC board as well as students of other standards who had demonstrated excellence in the academic year. As per the school's tradition, everyone associated with the school – be it past students in high-profile positions, retired staff and teachers, committee members – attended the function, as did members of the education ministry from state and central governments as Saraswati Vidhya Mandir had a high reputation in government circles.

Madhuri walked through the school gates. She was wearing a light pink sari with peacock blue lace. The glow of her pink sari reflected on her face, which had turned pinkish in the sunlight. Light make-up added to her beauty, and she had left her hair open that day. Whoever looked at her, found it difficult to look away!

She would be convening the proceedings of the function, and had prepared well.

The school ground was full of activities. She was surprised to see the crowd that had gathered outside the school gate. She also noticed police officers manning the entry at the gates, so though the crowd was much larger than that of every year, it was still orderly.

As the time scheduled for the function approached, the crowd grew larger, and soon all the seats were taken up in the seating area. She noticed the presence of the media in large numbers, something that had happened for the first time since she had joined the school. On one corner, she saw the hustle and bustle of quite a few people carrying cameras and microphones, who were engrossed in setting up their devices, preparations for transmission, etc. She realized that this year the school had caught media attention because of two reasons. First, technocrat and business head Rahul Saxena's association with the school and, second, the unique competition between the batch students of Rahul and Bhattacharya that had now become well known.

At one corner of the ground, opposite the school building, stood a large stage, measuring around 50ft wide and 20ft deep. A line of chairs and tables were kept at the centre of the stage, and a podium along with a microphone, stood at the left corner of the stage.

The entire scenario gave the impression of a grand function, all charged up with excitement and enthusiasm. At around 9.45am, police sirens sounded near the gate, announcing the arrival of VIPs.

Principal Sir strode towards the school gates. At the gate, he welcomed the dignitaries, shook hands with each one of them and led them to the stage. In the next 10 minutes, all chairs were occupied and every eye on the school ground was on the stage. Now that the bigwigs had all come and seated, the audience – mostly parents, students, relatives, and alumni – were getting restless, eagerly waiting for the function to begin. Fortunately, they didn't have to wait much longer.

Principal Roshan Daruwala looked at Madhuri and slightly nodded, giving her the green signal to start the programme. Madhuri walked on to the stage, to the podium and addressed the dignitaries and the audience.

"Good morning! On behalf of Principal Roshan Daruwala and the management of our school Saraswati Vidhya Mandir, I have the pleasure of welcoming our honoured guests from the education ministry of Maharashtra, led by Shri Sushilkumar Joshi, Secretary, Education Ministry; Mrs Padmavati Shetty, Member of Executive Committee, ex-Principal and author; Mrs Shailaja Shinde, Commissioner, Education Ministry, IAS officer; and Dr Premshankar Mahajan, Principal Secretary, Govt. of Maharashtra.

"Ladies, gentlemen and students, I am also pleased to inform you that for the first time in the history of our school, we are privileged to have with us Shri Pratap Kumar Sharma, Principal Secretary, Education Ministry, Govt. of India, New Delhi. Sir, we are delighted to have you amongst us, and we are grateful that you took out time from your busy schedule for us today. Ladies and gentlemen, please welcome the dignitaries with a big applause as we are honoured by their presence in our Annual Day."

The ground was filled with loud applause. After the applause faded away, Madhuri continued.

"I now request Shri Batliwala, our beloved chairman, to welcome our guests with bouquets of flowers as a token of our love and respect."

Batliwala got up from his chair and gestured Roshan Daruwala to join him. They walked up to the dignitaries, one after the other, and presented them bouquets of flowers. This was a moment of great pride for all those associated with the school, now or in the past, as this was the first time that so many luminaries were visiting the school on its Annual Day.

Batliwala came near the microphone and addressed the crowd.

"Good morning honoured guests, parents, teachers, staff and my dear students. I am delighted with the love and respect that you have bestowed on our school and our members of the staff. My grandfather built this school in 1950, which means, our school is 65 years young. Although I have been the chairman of this school for the past 25 years, never have we received so much respect and attention as we have today, be it from government executives, media, parents and the public at large. We are thankful to you all and hope you will continue to bestow the same love and affection in future as well."

There was applause from the stage as well as audience as Mr Batliwala finished his address.

Madhuri came up to the microphone and asked Principal Roshan Daruwala to say a few words. Principal Daruwala walked to the podium, and spoke into the mic.

"Good morning distinguished guests, students, parents, ladies and gentlemen! Today is the greatest day in the thirty years of my career when our school has received so much love and affection from all of you. We, at Saraswati Vidhya Mandir, have always believed in innovation and doing things differently which not only make learning more effective but also makes it more interesting for students.

"Last year, we experienced something very different! As you all know by now, Mr Rahul Saxena, renowned technocrat and visionary, joined our school as a member of the teaching faculty. A loving father, his love and concern for his son prompted him to take this decision. When he had approached me, I, initially, did not know what to do, because I was confused if such a high-profile personality would be able to do a teacher's job. But the power and sincerity of his appeal and the honesty in his eyes impressed me, touched my heart.

"From the very first day, Rahul adopted a very different approach to teaching. Unlike most of the other teachers in our school, he held teachers and parents responsible for the student's performance in academics. Rahul put forth a very valid point that when we are producing lakhs of engineers, doctors and management graduates, year after year, why are we not able to produce Einsteins or Newtons or Archimedes!

"He displayed unparalleled confidence in the capabilities of students, so much so that a competition was set up between one of our senior teachers and Rahul. We formed two batches; one consisting of above-average, brilliant students who had consistently topped their classes, and the other consisting of below-average students, as well as those coming from a poor socioeconomic background, from families that were financially incapable to support their education."

Principal Sir paused for some time. He looked at Batliwala who nodded at him, smiling encouragingly.

Principal Roshan Daruwala continued, "I am very happy to

inform you all that, all the students in Rahul's batch, despite their poor track record and delicate financial conditions, have performed beyond our expectations! Rahul's efforts and philosophy has introduced a very new belief system, a new methodology to our education community not only in India but all over the world. I am extremely proud that, Rahul has been chosen by Prime Minister Shri Narayan Mohanji to hold an important portfolio in the education ministry and spread awareness about his reformed teaching methodology so that every student can benefit from his ideas. We are happy to have a person like Rahul amongst us... I now request Rahul to come on stage and accept a bouquet as mark of our love and affection, and share his thoughts with us."

The audience was stunned for a minute. Then, Batliwala got up from his chair and started clapping. Slowly, the claps grew louder and louder, and one by one, the audience stood up. The standing ovation to Rahul continued for a while.

But the situation was different for Madhuri. She did not know how to react. While on the one hand she was very happy with the honour bestowed on Rahul, on the other hand there was the possibility that Rahul would leave the school, and will go away from her. Mixed emotions ran through her, which was evident from her eyes: wet but with a bright sparkle! She surreptitiously wiped her eyes.

Rahul who was sitting in the front row in the audience, got up, and slowly but confidently walked up the few stairs that led to the stage. He was wearing a grey stripped shirt and black trousers. Slim, and with a stubble on his face, he looked pale and weak. While walking towards the microphone, he smiled at the dignitaries, his head slightly bowed.

The cynosure of all eyes, Rahul adjusted the microphone with his right hand. He closed his eyes and chanted a mantra.

"*Guru Brahma, Guru Vishnu, Guru Devo Maheshwara! Guru Sakshat Para Brahma, Tatsamayi Shree Guruvey Namah*!!

"For ages, the teacher has occupied a unique position in our society, in our homes and our hearts. It is because of his unique position in our hearts, that we have accorded him the same status as we have given to Brahma, the creator of life, and Vishnu, the preserver of life. Such an esteemed position is well deserved for one who spends his/her life in shaping hundreds of lives of our children, year after year. They help us in shaping the lives of students, from the tender age of KG through adolescence, and finally to the stage where he/she is ready to face the world.

"A huge contribution indeed, which cannot be described in words. While parents give birth to the child and support him in terms of food, shelter and protection, it is the teacher who makes the child competent to face the harsh world, through knowledge and teachings related to character, patience and perseverance.

"It is due to such an immense contribution of the teacher in your child's life that our Vedas depict the deep bond and relationship between a teacher and his disciple. All of us know the stories of Rama and Vishwamitra; Krishna and Sandeepani; Arjuna and Dronacharya and many more. The relationship between a teacher and his disciple then was very healthy as everyone around the child was aware and obliged because of the huge impact that the teacher had on the child. Perhaps due to such bonding and relationship, the respect and special status accorded to teachers in our society in the ancient times, we got great and invincible personalities like Rama, Krishna and Arjuna!"

The audience was listening to Rahul with rapt attention. Rahul paused for a moment, looked around the audience and then continued.

"I want all of you to pause for some time and think. Are we giving the same status and respect to our teachers today? Perhaps the answer is NO. We have converted the teacher and his contributions to that of a commodity. We pay him for his services and that's the end of it. This situation is further hampered by people with commercial minds, such as some tutorial centres that sell knowledge to students for a huge sum of money. Taking advantage of the students' dream to get into a particular institute, they advertise with big promises. Politicians, trustees and other office bearers of schools and governments further compromise the status of teachers. There is so much pressure on the resources available with teachers that today he is not *Bhagya Vidhata* – fortune builder – but he is an ordinary servant of the society.

"I fail to understand, why today's teacher is weak, helpless and hapless. Sometime back, I had travelled to Patna in Bihar. I saw hundreds of teachers on the road demanding payment of their salary, due for over a year! In our own school, we have many teachers who are not able to afford a decent house for themselves. What a stark contrast! The commercial-minded society is full of economic geniuses but it's unable to evaluate and compensate the true worth of the contributions made by an honest teacher, who is either underfed or struggling to make two ends meet! And, on the other hand, commercial exploiters of education, on the strength of the money generated through enormous fees extracted from aspiring students, roam in Mercedes Benz! No wonder then that we don't have a *yug purush* like Rama or Krishna in recent times... because we have failed to value the

Vishwamitra or Sandeepani in our society. We have instead produced self-centred, money-spinning machines."

Rahul paused for a moment, sipped water from the glass kept on the podium and continued, "The other grave outcome of our negligence towards the teacher is that we are becoming a society full of *insecure people*! That's the reason why we are witnessing today a strained relationship between teachers and students. Every day we hear or read news of a teacher hurting a student or students beating their teacher to death! How can it be possible unless we have created deep frustration in the minds of either the student or the teacher that they resort to such actions? Friends, I think there is a lot more that we need to do for our teachers and students, should we wish our nation and the world to be a more progressive, peaceful and livable place. I came to this school not only out of my love and concern for my child, but also to create awareness in our society about our responsibility towards teachers. Their contribution in building our society is no less important than the contributions made by a scientist or a technocrat!

"I want all of you to think of how we can better utilize the capability of these sculptors who could help us build a great nation, a great world. A world where no one is insecure and hence no one wants to rule or dominate. No one is cruel and selfish, hence no one creates chaos and scarcity for the children on this earth who are dying due to hunger or cold. No mother on this earth should witness the pain of her womb being wasted due to the excesses of others. No childhood should be ruined at the hands of circumstances, which can produce an Adolf Hitler or a Mussolini or any terrorist who could celebrate the death of innocents for the satisfaction of their egos, or religious misinforms.

"Friends, we need to change the way we value and compensate the sculptors of our society and nation. We need to make them happy and satisfied, and lead a life of dignity. We need to create a socioeconomic structure where more and more youth is attracted towards the teaching profession. I have taken enough of your time. Thank you all for your love and support during my illness. Before I conclude, I just want to say a few words of Saint Kabir: *Guru Gobind Do No Khade, Ka Ko Lagu Pai! Balihari Guru Aapki, Jisne Gobind Diyo Bataye.* (I am facing the teacher and God, whom do I salute first. I realize it must be teacher as he had created my awareness about God). Jai Hind."

Rahul folded his hands and raised them to the audience. There was a big round of applause from the audience. Principal Sir got up from his seat and came near Rahul. He gestured to the audience to stop, but the clapping continued. Rahul requested the audience to give an opportunity to Principal Roshan Daruwala to speak. The principal then thanked Rahul and announced that the award ceremony would take place shortly.

After meeting everyone and accepting compliments from all those on the dais, Rahul searched for Madhuri but he couldn't see her anywhere. As he climbed down the few stairs from the stage, he saw Bhattacharya waiting for him at the last step. He embraced Rahul.

"Rahulbaba, I'm feeling very proud today. I'm flabbergasted by your thoughts and the respect you have towards all of us. I assure you that I will put in my best to move forward the torch of revolution that you have lit in this school, which will not remain restricted to this school only but also to all the schools in the city, districts and the state."

Rahul gave a tight hug to Bhattacharya, thanked him and moved ahead.

The rush of people trying to meet Rahul and shake hands with him made it difficult for him to move quickly. At the other end, he saw David Brown and Peter Hoffman waving at him, trying to catch his attention. Rahul walked towards them.

As he reached them, David warmly shook Rahul's hand, and said, "Great, my friend! We all talk several good things but you have put your thoughts into practice. I came here to make you an offer of joining Gold Star Electronics as the CEO. I wanted to offer you the best package so that you can once again take GS to great heights, but after listening to you today, I feel the education ministry can better utilize your skills. Like Roshan, I also feel I can't be selfish, so I have to let you go."

Rahul laughed loudly and said, "Thanks, David. You let me go, otherwise you are a hard nut. If you decided to have me, you would have made it happen at any cost. Anyway, jokes apart, thanks for your offer, but I want you to make another offer!"

David was surprised; he couldn't understand what Rahul was hinting at.

"What do you mean?"

"David, you have made tonnes of money from society, why don't you think of returning some of it to society?"

David thought for a while, and then asked, "Will US$ 100 mn be enough?"

"More than enough for a start… we also need learned and intelligent people like you to participate in this transformation process."

David nodded, "Good idea. Let me think it over. I will get back to you."

"Dad!"

Rahul looked around to see Sachin. Rahul had a broad smile on his face, as Sachin came running up and hugged his father. David and Peter wished both of them the best for the future, and left.

"Dad, I'm proud of you. I will come with you to Delhi."

Rahul could sense that Sachin was upset with the news of him joining the education ministry, and the possibility that he may shift to Delhi.

"Sure, son, but then, who will be with your mother? You are a big boy now, and need to be a guardian to older people like your mother and me, and besides, I'm not going there permanently; I will keep visiting Mumbai and call you over to Delhi during your vacations."

Sachin looked somewhat reassured and beamed at his father.

As they were chatting, Sachin suddenly said aloud, "Mum."

Looking around, Rahul saw Sheetal coming towards them. 'Oh my God! Ms Firepower has caught me,' he thought.

But to his surprise, a smiling Sheetal came up to him, and extended her hand to shake hands with Rahul.

"Congratulations, Rahul. I have misunderstood you for all these years. I'm sorry for the terrible time I gave you in the past."

Taken aback, Rahul said, "Are you the same Sheetal, Ms Firepower?"

Sheetal laughed, "Yes, I'm the same. Still with firepower, but not aimed at you or Sachin. I have realized that you can't win hearts by dominating others; it must be won through love and affection, and by becoming one with people."

Sheetal saw that even while she spoke, Rahul was searching for someone.

She said, "What you are searching for is here with me," and beckoned at someone to join her.

Rahul then saw Madhuri a few steps away from them; Sheetal reached out and gently drew Madhuri close to her.

She smiled, "You were looking for Madhuri, right?"

Rahul did not know how to react, and mumbled, "Yes but no, no."

"You don't need to hide your feelings for Madhuri, I know about it! As a matter of fact, what I couldn't give you and Sachin during our family's challenging times, has been given by Madhuri, I must admit."

Realizing Rahul's and Madhuri's discomfort, Sheetal spoke earnestly, "See, I'm a modern woman. I don't mind admitting that I failed in fulfilling my duties as a wife and mother. All that I have given you and Sachin was nothing but hardship and intolerance. I was available physically but could not give you the love, warmth and support that generally a husband would seek from his wife. Now when I think about it and look at how much Sachin has changed for the better, I realize that you were absolutely right in your decision to give up everything you had, for the sake of our child. At school, you had to start from scratch, and again I was not by your side. Here you met this little sweet lady, Madhuri, and she rekindled hope and confidence in both of you. She showered that much-needed love, warmth and affection on Sachin that today he is more inclined towards Madhuri than for me. I'm happy to have a friend and a well-wisher for life in Madhuri."

Rahul was speechless, as Sheetal seemed to be a completely different person.

Sheetal continued, "I have been an advocate all my life. But today, I want to be the judge – and none of you will go against my judgement!"

By this time, her voice had become heavy and choked. Her eyes too had become moist, but there was a smile on her face.

Placing Madhuri's right hand on Rahul's, she said, "Now she is your responsibility," then looking at both of them, "I will always remain your well-wisher and good friend.... Wish you good luck!"

She then turned around, and started walking towards her car.

Rahul called after her; Sheetal turned around and said, "Don't call me again. I have given my judgement! I don't want to impose our past relationship on your future, because in your journey ahead, you need a partner, who can forget her own identity and support you. I have seen that quality in Madhuri, so it is better that both of you remain together. I will always be there to support and pray for both of you. As far as Sachin is concerned, I am always there for him. Plus, he will find a new guardian and friend in Madhuri."

She turned her face away. Rahul knew that the tough lady that she was, she didn't want anyone to see her tears, not even Rahul. Sheetal opened the door of her car, sat in it, started the engine and drove off, waving at Sachin, Rahul and Madhuri.

Evening was descending on the ground. Slowly, as time passed, the crowd in the school ground grew thin. Rahul turned towards Madhuri and Sachin, and held their hands in his hands and they walked towards the school gates. They were all silent, but their minds were busy with many thoughts and mixed emotions. With each step that they took together, their thoughts settled down, and their grip became firmer, as if they were unwilling to leave each other's company, perhaps for generations together.

My dear reader friend,

Thanks for being my co-traveller in this journey, and I hope you enjoyed the journey. Through this book, I wanted to entertain, educate and inspire you to think and act in the direction set in this book, i.e., providing the right environment, care and encouragement to children, the foundation of our future.

I am also sure that, after reading this book, you would agree with me that no child or for that matter any human being is less intelligent or less capable. However, in our practical day-to-day life, we do come across human beings with obvious differences in their capabilities. This difference is due to the difference in the environment and the background they were born and nurtured. With patience, perseverance and hard work, we must try to improve on the environment we provide to the people around us, irrespective of their age.

This is the beginning of our beautiful relationship. I am keen to know how you liked the book. Please write to me at vkallola@gmail.com

There is nothing more rewarding for me in this world than reading your reviews and receiving your appreciation, which will encourage me to serve you with many more interesting stories in future.

To your health, fitness and happiness!

Vasant Kallola